AMIGO, AMIGO

AMIGO, AMIGO

FRANCIS CLIFFORD

Academy
Chicago
Publishers

Published in 1985 by

Academy Chicago Publishers
425 N. Michigan Ave.
Chicago, IL 60611

Library of Congress Cataloging in Publication Data

Clifford, Francis.
    Amigo, amigo.

    I.   Title.
PR6070.H66A84   1985   823'.914   85-1368
ISBN 0-89733-136-2

My name is Death; the last best friend am I.
—Robert Southey

Multis pro beneficiis multis.

One

Lorrimer was on a stopover in Mexico City, staying at the Alameda Hotel on the Avenida Juaréz and trying to make up his mind whether to reroute himself home to England via Los Angeles or New York. As it turned out he did neither.

"Mister Lorrimer?"

"Right."

"Mister Anthony Lorrimer?"

"That's it."

"May I speak with you, please?"

"What about?"

"It is confidential."

They were in the foyer and people were coming and going all the time, *click-clack* on the immaculate mosaic floor. The stranger who had touched his elbow was a head shorter than himself, anonymous behind dark glasses, narrow-faced, mouse-haired, with a lip-line mustache. He seemed uncomfortable, uncertain, with the heat of the streets still damp in his pores.

"Perhaps we could find somewhere more private," the man suggested. His English was good, though heavily accented. He swiveled around and gestured vaguely. "There is so much traffic here."

"D'you know the Café Monterrey?"

"Yes."

"I'll meet you in half an hour."

It is old and genuine, the Monterrey, with an interesting tile decor. Cool, thank God. And cheap. What's more—it hasn't been overrun by the tourists yet. Lorrimer went straight there and found a corner table, sufficiently apart to ensure privacy. At barely one o'clock the place wasn't more than a third full anyway. He lit a cigarette and waited for the man to come, wondering what he had to sell; his kind was never short of material, though only once in a while was it based on worthwhile fact.

"Am I late?"

He was older than Lorrimer had somehow remembered. He wore a blue lightweight suit that had seen better days and his pink cuffs were frayed. He sat down and shook a cigarette from the offered pack.

Lorrimer said, "What made you pick on me? I'm not the only journalist in town."

"I was given your name."

"Given?"

"Yes."

"Who by?"

"A friend." Then, by way of insurance: "A friend of a friend."

"Ah."

"He likes your work."

"That's very kind of him."

The man cupped his hands to the lighter flame. Smoke curled around his putty-colored face. He leaned forward as it cleared, as confidential as a pimp.

"What I have to discuss is unique and exclusive."

"Naturally."

"Truly. It is exceptional."

"No doubt."

"And accurate. One hundred percent accurate."

"I daresay. . . . Perhaps you'll come to the point. What precisely is this about?"

"A manuscript."

"Not interested."

9

"You would be."

Lorrimer shook his head. "I prefer to write my own."

"This manuscript needs editing. In that direction alone your help would be appreciated." The man moved a knife here, a fork there—small, nervous actions. He wasn't looking at Lorrimer. "It also needs someone to help market it, someone to act—"

"Me?"

"My friend believes so."

"Why not your friend himself? Or this friend of your friend?"

"Impossible."

"Why not you?"

"Impossible," the man said again.

"Too dangerous?"

"I am not qualified. As for those I represent. . . ." He narrowed his shoulders and sketched a small gesture. "There are difficulties."

"For the author?"

"Correct."

"Who is he?"

"I don't know him."

"I didn't ask that."

The man blew a jet of smoke and leaned a shade closer. Behind the dark lenses his gaze lifted briefly, then shied away.

"Riemeck," he said.

"Come again."

"Riemeck . . . Peter Riemeck."

"German?"

"Yes."

Lorrimer narrowed his eyes.

"I don't know him," the man repeated. "I am a long way down the line."

"Exiled patriot?"

Surprise parted thin lips.

"Onetime Nazi?"

"Yes."

"They're two a penny."

"Not Riemeck."

"No?"

"He was important. Very senior in the SS. Very active in Czechoslovakia and, later, Italy."

Lorrimer frowned.

"You are too young, Mister Lorrimer. If you were my age you would remember . . . Heydrich, for instance. You will have heard of Heydrich surely?"

"Heydrich, yes."

"Riemeck was for a while Heydrich's deputy."

"You make it sound like an honor."

The man began crushing his cigarette in the ashtray, switching his glance from side to side. But he needn't have worried; no one was within earshot.

"I have read this manuscript."

"So?"

"It is of worldwide interest."

"What an awful mistake it all was—is that the line he takes? Killing was the fashion then and I was one of the herd—is that how it goes? Or does he concentrate on how he's managed to resist being extradited from wherever he happens to be?"

"Neither. But he names names. It is the names that make this manuscript so significant."

"Bormann?"

"Bormann died three months ago." He was as plausible as could be. "Of cancer."

"Who then?"

"Mengele, for example."

"Old hat," Lorrimer said.

"Not for some."

"No one else?"

"Glucks . . . Alsen."

"Give me a name to make me blink."

Cunning disfigured the man's mouth. "The most startling details do not necessarily concern those who fled. Some of the major revelations concern former colleagues who remained in Europe or have since returned, the ones who successfully changed their identities. . . . Incidentally, not all are Germans."

A few seconds elapsed. Then Lorrimer said: "Are you eating?"

"Thank you."

The Monterrey specializes in Mexican food and a fixed price menu. As soon as they had ordered and the waiter had gone away, Lorrimer said with a snort of derision: "I can't think why I bother. A whole saga of make-believe has come out of South America during the past twenty years, and I don't see any reason why this should be any different."

"Who mentioned South America?"

He was quick, a shade too quick, but Lorrimer let it pass.

"Every instinct in me says you're peddling fiction."

"Oh, no." The tone was almost vehement. "Certainly not."

"Put yourself in my shoes. If I had—"

"Listen," the man cut in. He pressed Lorrimer's sleeve with nicotine-stained fingers. "I am in no way close to Riemeck. Many people separate us. I have never met him and never will. But I am assured this manuscript is genuine and that it deals only in the truth."

"And you are offering it to me on the instructions of a friend?"

"Correct."

"What's in it for you?"

"A fee—if I am successful. A small fee."

"But of course," Lorrimer said dryly. "What's in it for Riemeck?"

"Who can say? What he has written will cause a sensation. There are several people, some of them important and distinguished, whose lives have been acts of misrepresentation for a quarter of a century."

"And all at once Riemeck is ready to sell them down the river?"

"Circumstances change."

" 'My honor is loyalty'—wasn't that the motto of the SS?"

Silence separated them. Some of the other tables were filling up and the sense of conspiracy tightened. Laughter sounded through the surrounding drone of conversation. Outside, in the hot bright street, tires were whinnying out of a turn.

Presently the man said: "Are you interested?" He was looking at his fingernails.

"Not in a pig in a poke."

A baffled expression. "How do you mean?"

"Not without reading what's on offer."

"I am unable to let you do that . . . Unfortunately. Not at this stage."

"Then I'm not interested."

"There have to be safeguards. The person concerned has to protect himself."

"Jesus," Lorrimer said.

"In his position it is inevitable."

"There's another side to the coin. For all I know you've dreamed this whole thing up. Give me something to make a judgment on before you start asking whether I'm interested or not. For instance—what proof is there that Riemeck is actually responsible for the manuscript?"

"The proof is its accuracy. Fingerprint accuracy. Not a word is invention, Mister Lorrimer."

"So you say. But I'd need more than your hand on your heart."

The man seemed to have anticipated this. Without any sign of hesitation he said: "I can let you have a short extract from the text . . . A sample. You will be able to verify everything it says. Personally."

"In Europe?"

"No."

"I was planning to leave for Europe tomorrow."

"The extract I would give you concerns someone not all that far from here."

"How far?"

The man touched his mustache. "A few hundred kilometers?" He was giving nothing much away, but the place had to be south.

"Who is he?"

"Lutz Kröhl. At least, that is what he was." He paused momentarily, as if to heighten effect. "For something over a year Kröhl was in charge of camp administration at Auschwitz."

The waiter returned, setting plates in front of them, leaning over, oblivious of crimes and horrors long ago. The man delayed until they were alone again.

"The extract gives Kröhl's present whereabouts, occupation, the name he is living under and so on. Go and see for yourself, Mister Lorrimer. Europe can wait, surely? The accuracy of what I have in my possession will whet your appetite for more."

Lorrimer stared at the narrow face across the table, the creases, the lines, the drab, uneasy eyes.

"During Kröhl's time at Auschwitz upwards of a million people would have been killed."

"You can drop the propaganda," Lorrimer snapped. He had once made a tour of Auschwitz and it was hideous; for days afterward its ghosts had haunted his imagination. "All I need right now is about one thought too many in that direction to make me turn my back on you for good."

The man flashed him an obsidian glance, very quick, searching. The eyes told everything—always.

"Are you interested?" he repeated.

Lorrimer nodded. "Up to a point . . . But why me?" he asked. "Why not go direct to a newspaper?"

"The person concerned prefers to be represented."

"You mean Riemeck prefers."

"I am not in touch with Riemeck, so I cannot say."

"Why keep wrapping him up?" Lorrimer retorted irritably. "Even if you're not talking about Riemeck, I am. And he's sure to know there are agents who specialize in handling—"

"Agents are too remote."

"I would advise him to get one."

"Your advice is required in many directions, Mister Lorrimer."

"It won't be cheap."

"That will have to be discussed."

"You bet it will."

The man's mouth twisted.

Lorrimer said, "When can you let me have this extract about Kröhl?"

"Tonight."

"Bring it to the Alameda at eight o'clock."

"Very well."

They began to eat.

"There is just one thing," the man said carefully. "Do not make the mistake of assuming Kröhl's story is now your own property. That would not be very wise."

Lorrimer raised one eyebrow. "Is this some kind of a threat?"

"I am merely making it known that if you pirate the Kröhl information, you will exclude yourself from seeing the rest. And the rest is the cream."

"Am I a fool, d'you think?" Lorrimer forced a smile. "In any case I never pirate anything before checking on it first."

"I will give you a telephone number. When you return with confirmation of Kröhl's existence we will need to meet again."

"Always remembering I may not choose to go."

The man ignored that. "Before you can be entrusted with the complete manuscript certain safeguards will be necessary. Binding agreements will have to be entered into."

"You seem very certain we'll get that far together."

"I can't believe you will pass up such an opportunity." He might have been selling soap. "I tell you, Mister Lorrimer, what Riemeck has written is as devastating as it is truthful."

"Then God protect us from old friends," Lorrimer said, and watched the muscles clench in the hollow cheeks. "Even from old friends of friends."

Two

The man was in the hotel foyer punctually at eight, pigeon-toed and drawn-looking. He handed Lorrimer a brown quarto-size envelope, and his only remark was, "This is a translation made by me. I have also given you the telephone number I spoke of. Call me by noon tomorrow with your decision."

"Okay," Lorrimer said. "I'll do that"—and watched him walk away.

AMIGO, AMIGO

He turned and went up to his room on the fourth floor with its piped music and bright Matisse prints. The envelope felt as though nothing were in it, but when he slit it open he found it contained a single sheet of typing paper, the thin kind used for copies. What he read was as follows:

Karl Stemmle is now sixty-three years. He lives in a place called Navalosa. Navalosa is in the volcanic mountains of the Sierra Madre in Guatemala, about twenty kilometers from the border with Mexico. Stemmle does work as a dentist and has lived in this village for more than ten years. Before that he was in Bolivia. He reached South America by the same route and the same connections as Mengele and others. He now has Guatemalan citizenship.

Stemmle's real name is Lutz Kröhl, the same SS-Oberführer Kröhl who was responsible for records and administration at Auschwitz from the late summer of 1943 to December, 1944.

Soon after his arrival in Bolivia, Stemmle underwent surgery which altered the shape of his nose and shortened his lower jaw. In 1953 or thereabouts he was married to a widow in La Paz, but the woman has since died. "Stemmle" was not his alias in those days. As a cover he once used to claim that he fled Europe after suffering in concentration camps. To authenticate this, he had an Auschwitz camp number tattooed on his left arm, but the number did not match the records, which remain in existence. He vanished from Bolivia at a time when this matter was being investigated. The tattoo has since been obliterated by another —of a flower.

Lorrimer read it through twice, sitting on the bed. His first reaction was disappointment. Somehow he'd expected more. And he'd also expected somewhere closer at hand: Navalosa sounded like the back of beyond. He grunted, lit a cigarette, and reread the information slowly. Then he crossed to the writing desk and worded a message to London. First things first.

PLEASE CHECK AND ADVISE MOST URGENT LUTZ KRÖHL SENIOR SS OFFICIAL AUSCHWITZ 1943–44 STOP REPEAT LUTZ KRÖHL REPEAT MOST URGENT.

In five minutes the cable was on its way. He couldn't really expect a reply by the following morning, but for the moment this was his least concern. He stood at the window and looked out at the neon pulse of the city, restless and undecided.

Kröhl, Stemmle . . . it was quite a carrot. But he was jaded; until hours ago his mind had been firmly set on getting home. He had been four months away and the last few weeks had gone sour, two commissions falling through and a bout of fever putting him on his back when he should have covered the consequences of an earthquake in Peru. Free-lancing was a brute sometimes. Bogota, Quito, Caracas—he'd had his fill of alien cities for a while. It was May now and England was at its best in May.

And yet. . . . He turned to the sheet of flimsy paper once again. "A sample, Mister Lorrimer. Something to whet your appetite for more." Against his will he acknowledged a tremor of professional excitement. The information might be less than he'd anticipated, but it somehow carried the stamp of authenticity; a sixth sense evaluated these things and it wasn't often wrong.

Why single *him* out though? All he could come up with was the fact that three weeks ago the magazine *Now* had carried a piece he'd put together on the military strengths and abilities of eight South American countries. It was a sound enough product, well researched and carefully reported; together with the biographical note at the end, it must have caught the eye of whoever was advising Riemeck. "He likes your work. . . ." No other explanation was feasible, though it seemed a gamble for cautious men to make an approach on the strength of a one-shot feature.

He photographed the typescript before locking it and his camera separately away. Then he went down to the street and took a taxi to a club he knew. There, after eating alone, he watched the floor show and danced to marimba music with a tall, slim hostess whose eyes rarely left his face and whose sinuous body rippled with sensual abandonment. The eyes were like Sarah's, questioning, full of dark fire.

"You staying in the city long?"

He shook his head. "Just passing through."

"Haven't I seen you here before?" White teeth and *café au lait* skin. "Last night?"

"Could be." *"Es posible"* was how he put it.

"Where you making for when you leave?"

"England, I expect."

"Only expect?" It amused her. "You English?"

"Most of me."

"I thought so," she said.

"Why?"

She shrugged it away. Quite separately she said: "You don't talk much."

"I see more than I say. Two eyes and only one tongue—it stands to reason."

At the bar this was, perched on stools, sitting one out. A lot of the time he wasn't really listening. He kept finding himself trying to picture Kröhl, Kröhl now Stemmle, Stemmle now sixty-three, now supposing himself forgotten by the world, the surgery and the cold-sweat fears and the cyanide capsule in the hollow tooth all part of a nightmare blurred by the passing years.

The girl said, "Why aren't you sure where you're going?"

"It doesn't depend on me."

"Business, is it?"

"After a fashion."

He had no illusions; it was business, all right. If he took the bait.

In the morning he rang the number the man had given him and the voice that answered was immediately recognizable.

"You said you wanted a decision by noon."

"Correct, Mister Lorrimer."

"I need more time than that."

"How much more?"

"Another day."

A frenzy of scratching raced along the wire. "The friend I spoke of is expecting—"

"I'm on a tight schedule," Lorrimer lied. "Navalosa looks to me like eating into other commitments, so I need to be sure things can be rearranged."

"If you are having doubts or second thoughts about my approach, it would be better for all concerned if you turned it down here and now. As you yourself said, you are not the only journalist in town."

He had changed his style since yesterday, but he was bluffing and it showed.

"I'll ring tomorrow," Lorrimer said curtly and hung up.

He went to a bookstore and flipped through some maps of the frontier districts between Mexico and Guatemala. Navalosa wasn't marked in any of them. He pored over a road atlas at a downtown travel bureau, vainly searching the areas north and south of the Pan American highway well beyond where Navalosa was supposed to be. Finally he called in at the Guatemalan consulate and asked at reception if someone would be good enough to pinpoint the place for him.

"Navalosa?" The duty clerk stroked his blue chin. He didn't know either. He consulted a large physical map hung on the wall behind the desk, splayed fingers vaguely straddling hundreds of square miles of plains and foothills.

"It's somewhere in the Sierra Madre."

"Of course." The fingers slid through ninety degrees and began to spider about. Their owner peered, sometimes on tiptoe, a small, neat, courteous person in a well-pressed suit. "Navalosa," he muttered as if it were an incantation. "Navalosa."

Even on the map the terrain looked fierce, not easily accessible. The clerk searched patiently for a longish while before he eventually discovered what Lorrimer wanted.

"Here—Navalosa." He grinned happily, a successful explorer, and stood aside for Lorrimer to make closer examination. It was discouragingly remote. And high—near the sixteenth parallel. Nothing else was marked for miles around.

"Not many people," the clerk commented, lavish with gestures. Why anyone should inquire after such a place didn't seem to interest him. "Not much of anything at all."

Lorrimer nodded. "Thank you for your help."

"Is there more I can do?"

"No, thank you."

He returned to the Alameda and the faint air-conditioned hum of his room, where he once more read the notes about Kröhl-turned-Stemmle. He was hooked, no doubt about it. The thing was beginning to dominate his thoughts. As long as London didn't reply with a denial of Kröhl's existence, he was hooked. And Stemmle was only a beginning, a sample, a prelude to more dramatic disclosures. It stank, yet the potential helped to stifle his distaste for barter and betrayal.

Patience was never his strong suit, but there wasn't as long to wait as he'd feared. A cable arrived in late afternoon and it couldn't have been more positive.

CONFIRM DATES AND LOCATION LUTZ KRÖHL STOP WHAT ARE YOU UP TO NOW LONG TIME NO SEE STOP LENNY

Relief surged through him. He immediately bounced back his thanks, then called the given number. There was no answer. He waited about an hour before trying again, and this time he made contact.

"I've thought it over and the answer's yes."

"Everything tallies—right, Mister Lorrimer?"

He didn't demur; it must have been obvious what he'd really been doing. "As far as it goes. But Kröhl past is a very different thing from Stemmle present."

"Facts are facts, no matter the time and place." The pimpish voice was hatefully smug. "When do you leave?"

"In the morning."

"I wasn't expecting to hear from you until tomorrow."

"Better early than late."

"Exactly." The line was as bad as before. "Since we last talked I have had an opportunity to speak with my friend. He is anxious to have a firm understanding with you as soon as possible."

"I daresay."

"By the weekend. . . By Sunday."

Today was Tuesday. "I don't know about that," Lorrimer answered. "Navalosa's one hell of a place to get to. It's not exactly the stone's throw you implied."

"Fly to Guatemala City."

"That's the easy part."

"Take the bus out toward Quezaltenango and on to San Camilo. It is a good road, a good ride—say a hundred and fifty kilometers."

"And then?"

"There are connections . . . local services." He made it sound like the suburbs.

"All the way?"

"They will tell you in San Camilo."

"I'll need the five days," Lorrimer said. "I don't see—"

"My friend is not prepared to allow you more."

"Say that again."

"After Sunday," the man said, "we will go elsewhere."

He was running a variation of the selfsame bluff. It wasn't as clumsily obvious as before, but Lorrimer had no doubts.

"You've picked a crazy time to try and lean on me."

"Listen," the man said, risking a trace of command in his tone. "This Navalosa business was never intended to be more than an easily verified example of the quality of the manuscript. In view of the exceptional circumstances, most people would have accepted its authenticity on trust."

"Not me."

"Obviously."

"*You* put Navalosa forward," Lorrimer reminded him. "*You* had the extract ready."

"My friend has made it clear—"

"Why don't you say Riemeck has made it clear?"

"Riemeck is no longer the person's name, Mister Lorrimer."

"Surprise, surprise."

The wire spat at them both. The silence which followed prickled with hostility.

Then Lorrimer said, "I'll ring you before Sunday's come and gone. Guaranteed."

"Very well."

A sudden uncertainty possessed him, unease-inexplicable. He heard himself: "What's Navalosa like?"

"Like a hundred other places. Some houses, a church, a store, a *cantina*—the usual kind of thing."

"Were you ever there?"

"No," the man said, "but someone else was."

The phrase stayed with Lorrimer after he'd hung up.

He went into the bathroom and ran the taps and studied himself in the mirror. Someone was and someone would be. And he thought, God help you, Stemmle. It won't be long for you now.

If it's true.

Three

He packed a grip and booked himself on a morning flight. Around ten he checked out and went to the terminal for the airport bus. It wasn't very full—businessmen mainly, a couple of nuns, a gaggle of children; he must have begun a score of journeys with companions like these. And the airport itself was like a hundred others he had known and waited in: design different, layout different, uniforms different, but otherwise a counterfeit—the same measures with the baggage and the identical farce with passports, the same metallic-sounding announcements, even the same hijack procedures. Only the coffee was in any way memorable, something special, and he drank two cups before his flight was called.

Guatemala City didn't seem much of an attraction; the BAC-111 had more seats vacant than filled. He belted himself in, no one beside him, and felt the tension enter the airframe as the runway blurred and fell away. The airport tilted across his window, then leveled off, merging with the fringes of the urban spread, the detail dwindling, sharp and colorful in the sunlight but diminishing every second.

He had never been in Guatemala: east and west and north of it but never there. And he had never set out on something which carried such overtones. Orthodoxy was a dead end for the free-lance, and the past few years were littered with stories born of information privately received. But in all his experience there had never been an approach with the possible implications of this one. It intrigued and alarmed him when he toyed with what he might find himself involved with if Kröhl and Stemmle were in fact the same person.

If. . . . A part of him still doubted it. He was hooked, but he hadn't swallowed it whole. Not yet.

They flew southeast on a line somewhere between the peaks of Popocatepetl and the Sleeping Lady. Mexico slid smoothly underneath like a mottled expanse of crumpled parchment. Lorrimer lit a cigarette and thought about Stemmle, Kröhl . . . whoever. If nothing else, the man was expendable. A free gift on a plate. And the only penalty for using him was to be denied participation in further and more sensational disclosures—"the cream." Cash in on Stemmle and lose out on the rest—that was about it. Crude? . . . It was crude, all right, but coldly calculating and effective. "We want more than just a go-between, Mister Lorrimer. More than just an adviser. We want someone who has seen with his own eyes."

He closed them now, asking himself how Riemeck knew all he was said to know, and what had decided him to publicize it. Envy, was it? Poverty? Self-protection? Revenge? . . . One day, Lorrimer decided, he would get that story too. And there would be no room for pity when he did, or qualms of conscience.

"Otra cerveza, señor?"

"Huh?" He seemed to come back from a great distance. Smiling brown eyes, lacquered lips, a hint of perfume.

"Una cerveza?"

"Gracias."

He gazed at the retreating legs. "When they're ripe, the apples fall"—there was a Chicago feature editor forever fond of saying that, but Lorrimer chased the thought away. Not this time. No chance. Navalosa and return, and no more. He probed with his tongue around the lower front molars on the left side, searching out the cavity.

"You're a cunning bastard," Sarah had told him once. "There isn't a thing happens to you which you don't somehow put to use." Always a sting in the tail with Sarah. "If ever you got castrated, I bet you'd turn it to your own advantage."

In gaps between long smears of cloud Lorrimer thought he could decipher the Pacific coastline; to starboard, this was, about an hour after takeoff. They were eating by then. He took out the stuff about Stemmle and read it for the last time until it was firmly in his head, then he went aft to the toilet and flushed the information away. The trays were being cleared when he got back. Soon afterward they banked on a course correction and before long, looking at his watch, he reckoned they must have left Mexico behind.

There were no visible boundaries, no telltale changes of scene. The world below was lion-colored, pockmarked, verdigris-blotched, broken. And already they were leaving the high altitudes. He stared blankly past the starboard wing at tawny mountain masses and vast ravines and occasional townships encrusted like sores on the landscape. He yawned, stretched, pocketed the passengers' flight map. It was one o'clock and they were dropping more rapidly now, if anything a little ahead of schedule.

The aircraft bucked slightly as it met the up-currents. "No smoking, ladies and gentlemen . . . Seat belts, ladies and gentlemen. . . ."

Minutes passed, then the wheels powered down. They

came sweeping around on a slant above the crusted chancre of an extinct volcano, then straightened and shallowed onto their approach. A gauzy streamer shredded over the wing, and the runway beacons slid across the window as the pilot lined them up. Corn and sugarcane, some white walls and brown roofs, ragged children waving by a galvanized wind pump—these were glimpses, no more. Then the runway was under them and the aircraft was racing in to make contact with its own black shadow.

The sun seemed to hit him through a burning glass when he eventually started down the steps. He was carrying his camera and had his jacket slung: no luggage except the grip. He went into the cool of the cavernous reception building and stood in line at Immigration. Purpose of visit, length of stay, and so forth—all that. There had been a thousand frontiers with a thousand officials with eyes like these, watchful behind the apparent boredom. Lorrimer's lips curled as he passed through; it was all such a charade, additional tedium for the bona fide traveler. The ones the system was designed to single out made sure they went some other way—over, under, around the back.

Stemmle must have done.

"No tengo nada que declarar."

His grip looked shabby on the bench beside some of the matching luggage, and for once it was to his advantage. He was cleared without question. He walked through the doors onto the outer concourse, warded off the taxi touts and rode with most of the other passengers on his flight to the downtown terminal.

One thing was already sure: he hadn't a hope of getting to Navalosa before nightfall. In any case he didn't much want to arrive so soon and certainly not after dark. With more than four days in hand tomorrow would be time enough. But the earlier he made San Camilo the better. In San Camilo, with any luck, people wouldn't think he was asking about somewhere on the dark side of the moon.

"Navalosa?" On the run between airport and terminal an elderly man in the seat alongside had stared at him blank-faced and turned his question around. "Is it anywhere near Cobán? I'm from Cobán, you see."

At least he was able to direct Lorrimer to the bus depot. There were buses leaving for San Camilo both morning and afternoon, two a day, and he bought a ticket for the one due to arrive there right on top of the hour at six in the evening. All in all he reckoned he had done more hanging about than most, so an hour and a bit to kill was child's play. Mainly he watched the girls come and go, the city ones and those from the country, all sorts, dark- and olive-skinned, with and without destinations, and the more striking they were the more they noticed the weight of his scrutiny.

The bus he eventually boarded was packed, the suspension oversoft, and the driver intent on blasting a way clear with his horn. They crawled past the domed cathedral and the massive green-stone bulk of the National Palace. Only when they were out of the central grid of the city and had begun to pick up speed did the air seem to freshen. A large Indian woman in a cheap flowered dress was wedged in beside him. She had a live hare in her lap, its legs trussed back and front, and it stared at Lorrimer with terror as it quivered on her thighs.

He thought of Stemmle suddenly, imagined him, Stemmle who they said was Kröll; he would have known that kind of stare.

"Bueno," the woman remarked to Lorrimer with a gap-toothed grin, gesturing toward her mouth. *"Muy carnoso."*

The city petered out, finally running to seed among a crisscross tangle of minor roads and single-story shacks. They looped over a wide riverbed to join the Pan American, which headed northeast back to where he'd started from and far beyond. Mountains were all around. On the plateau between the mountains there were coffee and cotton plantations, and between the changing patterns of the crops the road swerved and cut its way, cactus along the verges, bare rock, parched scrub.

Periodically the bus stopped at villages and townships and people got on and off. At Chimaltenango, the first sizable town they came to, the Indian woman left with the hare dangling upside down from the crook of her arm. They cruised steadily with a rubbery whine, windows wide open, the air warm on their faces. The smells were of dust and woodsmoke, and the disk of the sun burned in a flawless blue sky.

Beneath drooping lids Lorrimer watched the shifting panaromas. A group of young rucksack-carrying Americans were at the back of the bus and their voices sometimes carried, anchoring him to the illusion that he hadn't yet quite left the world he knew. Jays screamed in pepper trees along the wayside and buzzards wheeled above the flanks of a volcano, but the earth had shrunk since the days when SS-Oberführer Kröhl came searching for a place to hide.

Lorrimer stirred, and studied the ghostly reflection of his face in the smeared window. Too much booze, too many casual women, too long without real roots; it all showed, every year a fraction more. He was thirty-seven but looked older, and though he could put his finger on the causes, he was lost for a cure.

Around five they quit the main highway. They had already climbed a little, but the horizon ahead looked a good deal more formidable. Purple shadows were beginning to stretch across the heavy swell of the land. A sign directed them away from Quezaltenango and they bypassed its sprawl, heading for San Camilo, trailing a plume of heavy dust. Some of the vistas were breathtaking and the Americans' cameras were busy. A few more villages came and went, offering fleeting sketches from life and broken architectural gestures from a colonial past.

Lorrimer smoked a cigarette and listened to those sitting nearest him. The Spanish he could follow, but the Indian dialect was meaningless, and this was what predominated now; everything had changed since they set out.

San Camilo showed at last. Lorrimer slipped his jacket on and waited for the bus to brake to a standstill and the driver to open the doors. Only a handful of people dismounted with him—men, mostly, none taller than his shoulder, chocolate-dark faces and velvet-black eyes under broad straw hats. They mooched away, leaving him standing, and only the Americans stared back at him as the bus moved off on the remainder of its journey to the Mexican border.

The sun was pushing long level rays in from the west, but it was cooler than he'd supposed. He crossed the square he'd found himself in, drawn to a PENSIÓN sign. A few kids came to beg on the way, but he wasn't having any. Sod off. "Know what?" Sarah had said. "There's ice in your heart when it suits you."

No one was at the reception desk when he entered the *pensión*'s doorway; an image of the Virgin was fixed to the wall behind. He slapped the brass bell and waited, and was eventually rewarded by the arrival of a middle-aged half-breed woman who pinned her hair as she faced him and said without enthusiasm: "*Sí, sí. . . .* There is a room, of course."

She climbed the creaking stairs and he followed her swaying rump. It was a narrow white-walled room off a long corridor, one flight up. Single bed, little furniture, naked bulb on a snake of electric cord—the effect was monastic. But it would do; he didn't complain. Worse was surely in store and the place was clean enough. Lorrimer showered off the day's dirt before returning to the entrance lobby and tackling the woman about what he most wanted to know.

"Navalosa?"

"Right." But for the Guatemalan consulate he might by now have begun to believe the place didn't exist.

"Navalosa is in the high country." *La tierra alta*—that, at least, he already knew. "Many kilometers."

"How do I get there?"

She said impassively: "Some of the way there is a bus. . . . *Most* of the way."

"When?"

"Every morning from the *plaza*. The bus travels as far as Macinta."

"And then?"

"You would need to walk, *señor.*"

"Far?"

"For some hours." Thin hands emphasized her vagueness. "I could not be sure about how many. Navalosa is not a place much visited."

He read the question shaping in her mind. "I'm a photographer."

"It is wild up there," she said. "The story is that God the Father made it when he was weary and did not care anymore."

Four

Dusk was swift and short-lived, heavy with the scent of oleander. Bats were already in erratic flight when Lorrimer visited the *cantinas* around the square. OLÉ JESÚS was picked out in electric lights across the front of the church, and a kneeling woman burned incense on the steps. In the second *cantina* he ate a dish of *carne asada* and swilled it down with thin cold beer, not spoken to as he ate but quietly studied, discussed. Tourists normally went on through.

Under the huge ceiba tree in the center of the square he bought a few pods of chili from an old stall-holder whose wizened lamp-lit face had the look of perished rubber. He took the pods back to the *pensión* with him, ran the tap over them, split one open along its length and placed it in the left side of his mouth between cheek and gum; it nestled there quite comfortably. Soon afterward he clambered under the mosquito net and set about going to sleep. He was tired and it didn't take long. But twice in the night he woke with his mouth on fire, and the second time he spat the chili out and swore and swilled his mouth with water—without much effect. It wasn't yet four in the morning, but further sleep was impossible. Restless and in pain he listened to the cocks begin to signal the approaching dawn and watched the darkness lose its hold.

The gum was inflamed and tender to the touch; later he examined it with rueful satisfaction in the room's spotted mirror. But the pain had lost much of its power by the time he checked out and boarded the bus for Macinta. It was a battered, ramshackle vehicle with slatted wooden seats and no glass in the side windows. An empty coffin was lashed to the roof—not, Lorrimer hoped grimly, as a routine measure. After yesterday's soft-spring comfort the noise and dust were hard to take, but he alone of the passengers seemed to be aware of the jarring vibration. There were fifteen or so others, all Indians, and everything about them evidenced the hard life—the coarsened skin, the ill-fitting clothes, the crow's-feet stamped at the outer corners of their sloe-black eyes.

The bus left about ten past nine, late, the driver still buttoning himself as he swung aboard. Within minutes they were climbing, the metaled surfaces left behind. To begin with, the gradients weren't out of the ordinary and they rattled along at some speed, but the driver was soon having to work repeatedly through the gears. There were crops as before, maize and coffee, sometimes potatoes, but the areas of cultivation dwindled. More and more there were empty expanses, mile upon mile giving birth to nothing but weed and rock, the slopes rising up to sharp-edged balding ridges.

It was an anaconda of a road. Lorrimer could see its grayish scar twisting over the contours toward a massive cloud-topped cone far ahead. And climbing, all the time climbing. He remembered two villages, miles apart, adobe walls and rust-brown roofs, thatch and corrugated sheeting, the buildings huddled together as if for protection. People got off as usual at these villages, but no one got on. Those who got off went burdened with loads of town produce—cloth, earthenware, tools—and women and children came to meet them, dogs sniffing excitedly around.

The coffin wasn't put down until Macinta. They passed a small lake, the water smooth as glass and midnight blue, boulders around the edges. There were only six in the bus by now, seven counting the driver, and the land they lurched and rattled through was mostly barren and un-tenanted.

Stemmle does work as a dentist and has lived in Navalosa for more than ten years. . . . Wait and see, Lorrimer told himself. Wait and see. Yet already he was sure of one thing: no one alien to such desolation would have endured it without cause. Ten years. . . . He winced at the thought and braced himself against a succession of potholes. One side of his mouth felt raw; gingerly he ran his tongue between cheek and gum. If anything he'd overdone it, but too much was better than nothing at all; the cavity alone was hardly enough.

Macinta clung to the slopes, bigger than the previous villages. The road went no farther; it ended with an abruptness that suggested that the builders had lost heart and given up. Chickens scattered as the bus juddered to a halt in a patch of shade, the radiator boiling like a kettle. The driver clambered onto the roof and lowered the coffin over the side to the accompaniment of sing-song jabber from those below. A smell rose up, compounded out of dung and human habitation, tobacco and horse piss, tannin and sweat. Nowhere was there any sign of grief.

"*Señor!*" The driver must have seen Lorrimer walking off. "You asked about Navalosa—"

"Correct."

"Take the track toward La Candela." He pointed in the volcano's direction. "You will see Navalosa well before you get there."

"How long will that be?"

"Three hours."

"Gracias . . . Adiós."

The track led where the road might have gone if someone had had determination enough. The air was noticeably thinner, and the heat trembled off the rocks and naked surfaces. There were few trees. It was almost noon when Lorrimer set out, and from the first he was stepping into his own shadow. An intense quiet soon enveloped him and the only sounds were those of his own making.

"Most people would have taken the information about Stemmle on trust"—he could see the putty-colored face, hear the voice. "The Stemmle sample is offered as typical of the manuscript's accuracy, and it is hardly likely therefore to be false." Balls, he thought. Crap. Only fools lulled themselves with "hardly likely"—and as often as not they came unstuck. "You're thorough, all right—I grant you that." Sarah again, turning a sentence as only she knew how. "Even someone who doesn't like you anymore would grant you that."

For an hour he was alone. He seemed to be heading for the absolute rim of the world. The track was a good couple of meters wide and there were ruts, so carts used it. Some of the time it made a deep ledge in the steep eroded slopes, and some of the time it followed a defile or a stretch where a stream had once come flushing down. It was toward the end of the dry season now and there was nothing in the stream-beds except snakeskin patterns of detritus.

After the first hour he saw in the far distance a figure astride a mule, but it was all of ten minutes more before they were close enough to greet each other.

"Buenos días."

The sketchy sign of the Cross was the only indication the stranger was a priest. Swarthy face beneath a battered straw hat, sandals and open shirt, calf-length trousers the kind the locals wore. The smile was warm, the tone curious but friendly.

"Americano?"

Lorrimer shook his head. *"Inglés."*

"That makes you far from home."

"I go where the work takes me."

The mule stomped the ground, wanting to be gone. "What kind of work, *señor?*"

"Photographer."

"Is that so?"

Lorrimer's camera was nothing out of the ordinary, but it wasn't much of a risk to assume the priest would fail to differentiate between his Seikord Special and, say, a Hasselblad. He said, "I'm completing a feature on the volcanoes of Guatemala." The lie came pat, prepared in advance. "La Candela is part of the program."

"Ah—La Candela."

A small silence ensued, moments of mutual uncertainty. Lorrimer wiped sweat from his face and the mule blew through its nostrils.

"The nights are cold in the mountains," the priest said. "You would need to stay in Navalosa if you hope to make the return journey to the crater in the same day."

"That is my intention."

"Then you are welcome at my house."

"Thank you."

"Tell the woman when she comes to the door that you met me on the way and she is to provide for you."

"You're very kind."

"Today I have to be in Macinta—for a funeral. But tomorrow I shall be returning to Navalosa. If we could eat together under my roof it would give me much pleasure. New faces do not often come our way up there." He twisted in the saddle, sweeping the horizon with his hand. "Some parish, eh?"

"How long has it been your responsibility?"

"Years." He sounded wistful. "I have stopped counting. When you eat with me you must tell me about the world."

It was on the tip of Lorrimer's tongue to mention Stemmle. Was someone of that name there? What age would he be and what did he do? Stemmle, yes, German, with a flower tattooed on his left forearm. Since when had he lived in Navalosa? . . . Many times afterward Lorrimer was to ask himself what might have happened if he had

47

merely verified Stemmle's existence, taken the priest's word for it, and turned around and started back to Mexico City. But that wasn't the way. Not his way. He needed to see Stemmle for himself, hear him, touch him; only then would he believe.

He said: "The world is the same as it always was."

"You must refresh my memory." The smile was there again. "Not only mine." Lorrimer read more into those three words than the priest could possibly have known. "Good-bye for now."

"Hasta la vista."

The priest flipped the reins and the mule moved on. Lorrimer followed suit. Twice he glanced over his shoulder at the dwindling shape shaken by the heat, but when he looked a third time a bend in the track had taken the priest from view, and Lorrimer didn't turn his head anymore.

He met no one else. About an hour later, in obedience to the bus driver's word, he got his first sight of Navalosa—a smudge below the skyline to begin with, as compact as a bird dropping, separated from the volcano's slopes by a series of splayed earth-folds. He blinked sweat from his eyes, perspective dramatically emphasizing the village's isolation. For another twenty minutes the track looped and twisted so much that, if anything, he was taken farther away, but then it suddenly seemed to make up its mind and curved in a long sweeping shelf across the face of the hillside.

From that point on, little by little, Navalosa began to disclose itself.

He was comparatively near—a mile, maybe—when he came over a false crest and discovered he was entering a shallow saucerlike depression, the village packed tight on its far side and areas of cultivation spread like a ragged patchwork almost everywhere else.

From lower down none of this had been visible. It was midafternoon now and his step was dragging. For perhaps the hundredth time he changed the grip from one hand to the other and sweated on, only the trained observer in him still alert. He passed through a corridor of shoulder-high corn, zigzagged across undulations of boulder-strewn mesquite, and finally reached his destination between low crops and a scattering of stunted pines.

At first appearances the place seemed dead. No movement, not a sound. The track frayed out into an arc of wasteland, then funneled back into a gap between some outlying buildings—shacks, mainly, unredeemed by the splashes of morning glory and color-washed planking. By the time the track had become what amounted to a street, he was almost into the *plaza*. A cat uncoiled itself from an angle of shadow and made off; a handful of loungers eyed him from the darkness of open doorways. Somewhere, muffled, he thought he heard music. He walked between dried mud walls and tile-ribbed roofs, the ground rock-hard beneath its coating of dust, the air sweltering.

He stopped as he entered the *plaza*, stopped and looked about him. This was it then. Welcome to Navalosa. . . . Christ.

The open space was rectangular, centered on a stone fountain. Weeds dotted the expanse of broken paving. Along two sides was a covered sidewalk, facing inward. At one end there stood a squat square windowless building which, Lorrimer guessed, was possibly a granary. At the other end was a church, daubed white, its iron-studded door bleached by the years, a green-black bell hanging against the sky in an open arch.

The lack of a sound, the extraordinary stillness, conveyed an immense permanence, almost frightening in its intensity. He went to the fountain and stuck his face in the cool clear water. For seconds on end he kept it immersed, then he straightened and gulped a breath, shaking his head, beads of moisture flying like a broken necklace. As his ears unclogged he thought he heard a voice behind him. He turned doubtfully, blinking, and saw a small child—pot-bellied, naked except for a short stained vest —indisputably a boy.

"*Dinero*," the boy said, cupping his hands and coming nearer. *"Dinero, por favor."*

Lorrimer picked up the grip. "Where is the priest's house?"

The boy stopped and stood his ground, stubbornly repeating his demand. Lorrimer glared at the belligerent brown eyes in the dark, snub-nosed face. Even here, he thought.

He said roughly, "Take me to the home of the priest. Then I'll give you money."

Five

The boy led him out of the *plaza*, three
paces to Lorrimer's one, bare feet scuffing the dust. The
side walls of the granary were covered with defaced elec-
tion posters belonging to another kind of world; now they
flaked like scurf on the whitewash glare. Lorrimer
followed the boy around a couple of corners. Somewhere
in the afternoon heat a baby screamed as if its throat were
being cut and he once more heard the tinny throb of

music; but apart from himself and the boy life remained altogether withdrawn.

In a shadowy slot between single-story buildings the boy suddenly halted and thumped a door.

"Here?" Lorrimer said.

The boy nodded and held out his hand. Lorrimer gave him a coin which he tested between his teeth before scampering away. No one came to the door, so Lorrimer knocked and this time there was a response. A bolt was drawn and a crack appeared, and in the crack he made out a segment of face, with small suspicious eyes between black plaits of hair.

"Yes?"

"I met the priest on the way. He said to come here."

He felt the woman's gaze move over him, down to the incongruity of his town shoes.

"Two hours ago," he added as a postscript. "He told me I would be welcome at his house."

"If the priest said that, *señor*, then I take you in."

She was in no hurry. A chain rattled and the door was swung wide. Lorrimer stepped into the enclosed gloom, nostrils flared against the smell of living. As his vision adjusted, he saw that he was in a crowded room—papers piled on a desk, pottery stacked on a table, a red and black rug draped across a low bed. There was little space to move. Some wooden chairs, a slab where a fire could burn, books, photographs, a crucifix pinned to the plain wall—most of a man's existence was here.

"Come," the woman said.

Lorrimer moved crabwise past the obstacles. Each wall had an opening in it. The woman went to one of these and pulled aside a curtain of beads. Lorrimer ducked through into another room, more like a cell, just large enough for a bed and a solitary chair. A narrow window let in light.

"I can give you coffee," the woman told him. She was bent and ugly, with eyes yellowed by many fevers. A priest's celibacy was safe with her.

"Thank you."

"And beans."

"Thank you."

She went away. He heard a clatter, the scrape of a ladle. He explored until he found the latrine in a walled enclosure at the back of the house—two poles and a pit; it was absolutely basic. He could wash himself under the same low roof; there were buckets of water and a chipped enamel bowl. When he came back into the confinement of the house, he hadn't long to wait before the woman brought the promised coffee and a dish of beans. There was rice mixed in with the beans, together with some fatty chunks of pork. He was hungry enough to have eaten anything, and he scoffed it all down and drank the sharp black coffee.

"All right?" the woman inquired, standing just inside the room.

"Good." He nodded.

Then he winced; deliberately he winced and touched his jaw.

"Too hot?"

"A tooth." He made a dismissive gesture, careful not to overreact. "It's nothing."

"Hell can be a tooth . . . I know," she said. She exposed empty shriveled gums. "I suffered once."

"Everyone suffers," Lorrimer said. "Toothache and death and taxes—there's no escape." He winced again. "Fine time to have it happen."

"The dentist will put it right."

El dentista nuestro was what she actually said, *our* dentist. His senses quickened, yet he was careful to appear to misunderstand.

"It can wait." He chewed the soggy beans and rice. "Three more days and I will be in the city."

"People come to our dentist from all parts of the high country."

Lorrimer pretended not to hear. He swallowed and made busy with his tongue. The woman turned and pushed through the bead-curtain. He let her go. Not yet, he thought, not quite so soon. He drained the coffee and went into the cell she had given him. For an hour he lay on the hard bed, eyes closed, curbing his impatience. So far, so good. Between four and five he got up and called to the woman, not loud, passing into the main room as he did so.

"Are you there?"

He heard a scuffle somewhere at the back of the house. Then she came, impassive, used to being at beck and call.

"Qué pasa?"

He began: "You spoke about a dentist—"

"True."

"How long would it take me to reach him?"

"Is the pain worse?"

"Worse, yes."

"The dentist is here, *señor*. In Navalosa. He is our dentist."

"Here?" He made it sound stupid.

"Here." She nodded. "Five minutes from where we stand." She gave him directions, drawing the route in the air. "He is a foreigner, like yourself, *un extranjero*."

"His name?" Suddenly Lorrimer had to know. "What name—?"

"I forget," she said. "Something strange . . . I never remember. What he does is the important thing." Her hands started up again. "Go left, then right, then right a second time. . . ."

He thanked her and withdrew. Yes, he thought. *Yes. . . .* It would have shocked him now if the pieces didn't fit. Stemmle was here all right. Almost for sure. Only a freak of chance or coincidence was going to prove otherwise now. Stemmle, Kröhl-that-was . . . Lorrimer slipped into his jacket and let himself out. Left and right and right again, through narrow earthen streets no wider than alleys, people beginning to stir, some aware of an intruder. A few emerged behind his back as he walked and he listened to their murmurs and felt his isolation even more than in the silence of his arrival. A dog came yapping at his heels, pigs rooted in a heap of communal waste, an obscene turkey barred his path, its purple membrane quivering with hostility.

"*Vete!*"

He kicked at the dog, drove the turkey away. The priest joined Stemmle in the hot maze of his thoughts. You needed to love your fellowmen to choose this place; either that or you were afraid of them. One of the two. God, yes.

He reached an open stretch the woman had described. Beyond it was the house. It stood alone among a patch of prickly pear, and its scabrous walls were leprous white under a low roofing of thatch. La Candela formed the distant skyline, and its old dead ash was everywhere like a powder. When it rained, Lorrimer reckoned, the area would turn to mud. He folded a handkerchief, pressing it against his cheek, and followed the worn path to the house. There were bars on the windows and a spray of dried flowers fixed to the door. Cornhusks crackled under foot.

"He isn't here."

Someone must have heard him coming. It was a female voice and it reached him through the nearest window. He narrowed his eyes and tried to see who had spoken, but without success.

"Not here?" he parried.

"No."

He searched the sepia darkness behind the bars. "I have a bad toothache. . . . *Un dolor terrible.*"

"Telling me won't make it any better."

Young, surly. He frowned. "Who are you?"

He stepped to the window and peered in, and as he did so the door was opened. She was dressed *ladino* style, blouse and skirt, and was lighter skinned than pure Indian, almost olive. Eyes like jet and blue-black hair, shoulder length. She leaned against the frame of the door.

"He isn't here," she said again.

"Where then?"

"Over the ridge." Languidly she moved an arm.

"Far?"

"A day's journey."

"When will he be back?"

"Tomorrow at sundown."

She said it with a kind of mulish insolence that inflamed Lorrimer's disappointment. He swore silently; by tomorrow evening he'd intended to be well away. The girl studied him with blatant interest, toying with a rope of beads slung around her neck.

"Where are you from?"

"Right now?"

She shook her head. "What nationality?"

Irritably he said, "English."

"He is German."

"Who cares?"

Piece by piece it was coming. Half in the shadow of the thatch a lizard flicked its tongue.

"I thought you might be German, too."

"English."

"He has Guatemalan papers," the girl said, "but he is what his parents were. Papers can't change that."

"And his name is—?"

"Stemmle." She didn't pronounce it correctly, but it clinched everything. "Karl Stemmle." Then, with a hint of contempt, she said, "He is old now."

Lorrimer shifted his weight from one leg to the other. The girl was barefoot, taller than the usual run. Her nipples poked their firmness through the plain cotton blouse. The face was oval-shaped, the lips full, the nose only a little flattened. At most she was twenty-five—and Stemmle was sixty-three. Almost anywhere else the inducements would have been more obvious; here, Lorrimer could think of none.

She said to him, "I can give you something for the pain."

"Such as?"

"A drink." Take it or leave it. "A little spirit."

"All right."

Hinges screeched as she pushed the door wider. He stooped to enter, following her through, and looked about him at the squalid severity of what he saw. By comparison the priest had it easy. Almost nothing on the walls, soiled matting on the floor, a few stools, a solitary table, a kerosene lamp, a plywood radio. . . . Alone in a corner of the room there stood an old dentist's chair and a treadle drill contraption together with a metal filing cabinet.

The girl left Lorrimer alone for a moment, returning with a bottle and glass.

"Here."

It was tequila, a third of a bottle only, water-clear. He poured a sizable measure, watched by the girl. Her blue-black hair had a shine to it, a natural gloss, and her eyes glistened like wet stones.

"What brings you to Navalosa?"

"The volcano."

"Are you a scientist?"

"Photographer."

"La Candela is dead," she said. "For a long time now it has done nothing. It will disappoint you."

"Perhaps."

Lorrimer knocked the tequila back, felt the bite and the glow. The girl went to the radio and switched it on; music filtered into the barren room from another end of the earth. Nasally, a voice sang:

> *In the land of the blind*
> *The one-eyed man is king. . . .*

"Take some more spirit."

Lorrimer unscrewed the cap and tilted the bottle over the glass. His frustration was easing. He'd as good as got what he came for. Curiosity, more than anything, had wanted a confrontation—and it might make him wait for it yet. But if he were to leave, and head as if for the crater and circle back to Macinta, he wouldn't have journeyed in vain.

Name, occupation, nationality—the **essen**tial facts were all confirmed.

He said casually: "What age is the German?"

"Are you afraid his hand will shake?"

He didn't know how to answer. The girl's gaze was steady and unblinking.

"How is the tooth now?"

"The pain is less."

"Will you wait for him?"

"I don't know . . . It depends."

"You can stay here."

"My things are at the house of the priest."

She pouted almost angrily. He drank the tequila and looked about him at what Stemmle had endured for a decade. Nothing stirred in him, no sense of commiseration. Stemmle was Kröhl, SS-Oberführer Kröhl. A time always came when you paid for yesterday.

"How old is the German?" he asked again.

"Too old."

The girl had moved quite close. Now she turned, unbuttoning her blouse, a crescendo of tension in the swiftness of her fingers, pinpoints of darkness suddenly alight in her eyes and her lips full and parted.

"Old is useless."

For a moment Lorrimer was taken unawares, but then something heaved and raced inside him and he thought: Why not? Why the hell not?

Six

She led him into another room, urgently, with nothing more said. There were packing cases in this room, draped with a blanket, and a bed made out of mats, but he hardly noticed. Everything they did was swift and wolfish, and the only sound she made was at the last, in the frenzy as he lost himself in the staring wildness of her eyes.

And when it was over and he lay beside her strong limp

olive body he knew for sure he wasn't the first to be here when Stemmle was away. "Don't you ever feel ashamed?" Sarah had once shouted, following him about the apartment. "Or are you different from other men? How is it you're apparently spared even a fleeting moment of remorse?"

What you remembered, and when. . . .

The girl said: "Toothache does you no harm."

The air in the room was absolutely still and the light was going, but she was turned toward him and he could see her very clearly. Her face was expressionless, and it was impossible to tell what she was thinking. She had an arm thrown across his stomach and her breathing had slowed, but a bluish vein in her neck continued to throb. On the wall behind her were pictures torn from magazines. Presley was among them, McQueen, Belmondo, a dozen more, and dog-eared movie magazines were scattered on the floor beside the heap of mats which made the bed. Lorrimer's gaze drifted back to the girl, her fierceness still fresh with him, a weal on his neck stinging from her nails.

"How long have you been here?"

"With the German?"

"Yes."

"Two years."

"Why?"

She delayed her answer. "He provides" was all she said.

Then: "Tell me about where you live, the places you go . . . *Como se llama usted?*

"Lorrimer." She practiced saying his name a couple of times. 'It is months since a stranger came to Navalosa."

"Small wonder. You're off the map."

"We had a prospector here at the end of the rainy season, but no one since."

Lorrimer recalled an exchange in Mexico City. "Were you ever there?" he'd asked, and the man had answered, "Not me. But someone else was." So was that when and how?—ostensibly as a prospector?

"Did this prospector stay at the house?"

"Yes."

"Like this?"

"No," she said, without a flicker. "What do you think I am?"

The light was shrinking fast. He started to get up but she restrained him, holding him, eager with her hands again.

"Not yet," she said. "Not so soon."

He freed himself, pushing away, lust dead and done with.

"Tomorrow night he will be home. Not now."

"I know that."

"Well, then?"

"No," he said.

The girl's eyes smoldered. She lay naked in the gloom,

with her dreams pinned about her on the wall, and
watched him dress, resentment in the corners of her
mouth.

"I hope the pain returns." Like a petulant child. "I
hope you have it worse than before."

"It comes and goes," he said evenly, buckling his belt.

"Only when it suits you, I think."

To placate her he said: "You underestimate yourself."
In Spanish it didn't come easily off his tongue. He kicked
into his shoes. "Good-bye, then."

It was like leaving a whore—and had been as quick.

The room he crossed on his way out was all shapes and
shades of shadow. He emerged into the open and took the
path between the clumps of prickly pear. Some boys
sniggered as he passed, and one of them said something he
didn't catch, but he could have made a guess; the snig-
gering told all. Not that he cared. He went out and entered the maze that led back to the priest's house. It
wasn't quite dark yet, but lamps were burning in the
village now, orange and yellow, and he could feel the heat
draining out of the air. A thin stick of a man moved from
one hut to another with a burning ember, and Lorrimer
caught the smoky whiff of it, met other men carrying hoes
and machetes, heard the hum of voices from a *cantina,*
stood aside for a string of laden mules to be led by, dust
lifting in the narrow street from the thud and scrape of
their hooves.

The place had come alive with evening, but except at

close quarters he didn't attract attention. And he was getting his bearings. At one point, by a turning, he glimpsed the whiteness of the church and part of the *plaza*. When he reached the priest's door, he knocked and waited as he had the first time, while a dog lifted its leg against the wall.

"*Señor?*"

"Correct."

A chain rattled as before, a bolt was drawn, a lamp showed in the vertical gap.

"Did you find the dentist?"

"He isn't there."

"*Ayeee. . . .*"

"Not until tomorrow."

Inside, almost everywhere was dark from the waist down and the woman's face was disfigured by the closeness of the lamp. She peered at Lorrimer and instinctively he touched his cheek, the charade not ended yet.

"What will you do?"

His shrug was a kind of shorthand. "I have taken some spirit," he explained. "Tequila. . . . It helps."

She muttered something and placed the lamp on the priest's desk. A fire glowed on the slab of stone beyond the low bed and the place reeked of smoke. The crucifix over the desk showed a figure with one hand torn away from the nail and lifted in sorrow and despair; the world, it said, would never learn.

"Did you meet the girl where the dentist lives?"

"It was she who gave me the spirit."

"She has a bad reputation, that one," the woman said. Small eyes, like a bat's, tight lips, thick plaits hanging down. "She dishonors him."

"Is that so?"

"It is common knowledge. I should not talk about it, but it is a shameful thing. The dentist is a good man, a fine man."

Lorrimer stifled his surprise. "In what way?"

"In every way," she said. "For one thing, *señor*, he has a respect for those who suffer."

Stemmle? *Stemmle?*

"He is not only our dentist, you understand. He is also our *curandero.*" Medical dabbler, quack. "And he does not ask for money first, the way many do. Often he does not ask at all. He has done this village very great service, *señor*, but the girl's behavior takes from his dignity. That is a sad thing to happen to any man."

"The remedy is his," Lorrimer said. The feel of the girl was on his body still, but he had no regrets. He wasn't responsible to Stemmle. "He can always turn her out."

"He doesn't know what she is, *señor*." An insect whirred against the lamp. "He is elderly and the girl is his weakness. He is devoted to her—unfortunately. The priest has spoken to the girl, of course, many times, though without effect. The girl should not be in the house at all, it goes without saying, but the priest cannot find it in him to inform the dentist of what happens behind his back." The woman made small flapping motions with her hands. "It is a dilemma for the priest, *señor.*"

"Time will resolve it."

"That may be."

"Only the dead keep secrets forever."

She lit a second lamp, and he took it into the place where he had left his grip. "Insensitive bastard"—the accusation echoed from the past, and he thought: All right, all right . . . Curiosity had got the better of him. Vengeance, justice—he wasn't concerned. But he had to wait for Stemmle now. *Had* to. On no account would he settle for less—despite its being Thursday already, despite the deadline.

A good man, a fine man, a man with respect for those who suffer. . . . It was an incredible thing to have heard. Ridiculous, monstrous. When, as the priest believed, the graves opened and the dead walked, a resurrected horde would deny it. And, until such a day, the truth was recorded in documents galore.

Lutz Kröhl, born-again-Kröhl. How could Kröhl conceivably be dishonored?

The first stars were already trembling in the deepening purple of the night; through the window slats Lorrimer stared at them and thought of the girl for a while, and the suddenness of it, and the rest. Then the bead-curtains rattled and light moved in bars across the wall as the woman came from wherever she had been.

"I can give you coffee, *señor.*"

"Thank you."

"Tortillas also, if you want."

There's nothing more, her tone implied. He wasn't hungry and he declined, but he took the opportunity to offer her money, more than enough to make sure she wasn't out of pocket because of him, and she accepted it without demur, without thanks even. But her gratitude showed itself in practical fashion. With the coffee she brought a coverlet for the bed. He refused her offer of a powder to ease the imagined toothache, but later she returned with a full bottle of tequila, which she placed on the table in the main room, and told him it was there. She must have left the house for this, he decided, but the radio she quite clearly remembered in an afterthought as something the priest possessed. It was a tinny plastic-cased transistor, very run down, and he used it to keep the silence and the small sounds of the house at bay. Mainly it pumped out Latin American rhythms, but once in a while there were voices which established that it was tuned to Guatemala City.

Presently he went back into the other room. The tequila was amber with age, and as before he drank it straight, without lime or lemon or pinches of salt. He used it as a refuge from the earliness of the hour and being alone in the cluttered area where the priest worked and slept his life away, with just the lamplight and the bottle and the radio for company. One month in Navalosa, Lorrimer told himself, and he would either have gone mad or drunk himself stupid.

A newscast held his attention. France continued to use the Pacific as a nuclear-testing ground; in the States there was severe flooding northeast of Florida; Spain had devalued the peseta. . . . It all seemed remote somehow —unreal. In Guatemala itself, fire had destroyed an apartment block in Puerto Barrios and bandits had raided the National Bank at Zacalocas. . . . More than once the machine-gun rattle of the Spanish had Lorrimer floundering, and when a note of unbridled passion began to inflame the reading of innumerable football results he switched off the radio.

None of the priest's few books was readable. He drank the tequila slowly until the bottle was half empty and the lamplight was furred around the edges. The woman came in once to tend the fire glowing on the slab, but after that she vanished for the night. There was a chill in the air when Lorrimer went out and used the pit. The stars were enormous now, the silence all-embracing. For what seemed a long time he delayed before returning inside, thinking back, thinking forward.

There are moments in life when a door opens and lets the future in. "Mister Lorrimer? Mister Anthony Lorrimer?"—that moment in the Alameda had surely been one. Time and chance had brought him here, along with disbelief and doubt; but certainty had taken over and only curiosity remained. And tomorrow offered an end to that.

An owl screeched as Lorrimer turned to enter the house, and his neck hair bristled. A sense of unease, of menace, touched him as it had once before and he wondered why. Stemmle's days were as good as numbered and he felt nothing on that score—nothing. Sarah was right about the ice-in-the-heart thing; it was a professional's hallmark. . . . So whatever intimation had brushed his nerves wasn't on account of Stemmle.

Who then? What then?

Seven

The priest was back in the morning. The first Lorrimer knew of his arrival was hearing the *clop-clop* of the mule in the yard at the rear of the house. It was around nine by then, so he must have left Macinta early.

"At dawn," he told Lorrimer.

This was after the woman had prepared breakfast; coffee and tortillas—they were almost an inevitability.

Dismounted, the priest was not as large a man as Lorrimer had imagined. His dark hair was clipped short to the shape of his head and his slightly sunken eyes were brown and eager and observant. He was also very talkative, as if the luxury of eating with a stranger had excited him. Lorrimer gave him the benefit of the doubt and put him on the right side of fifty.

"The woman tells me you went looking for the dentist."

Lorrimer nodded. "I'll catch him this evening. The pain's not as bad as it was. I'll go up to the crater and see him when I return."

"And tomorrow travel to Macinta?"

"Tomorrow, yes."

"And the next day?"

"With luck I'll be in the capital."

Something showed in the priest's eyes that seemed like a fleeting glimpse of longing, swiftly put down. As if to distract himself he reached across and switched on the radio. "Greetings on Friday morning," a brisk urban voice began as the station signal ended. And Lorrimer reminded himself that the day after tomorrow was Sunday, and by Sunday, in fact, he needed to be out of the country altogether and safely in Mexico City.

"How long do you intend spending at the crater?"

"That's difficult to say."

"The round trip will take you in the region of seven hours—on foot, that is. You can ride my mule if you wish, but I would not recommend it."

"Thank you"—Lorrimer smiled—"but I'll walk."

"You are wise, believe me. This mule has what is called a mind of its own, and I fear that it will already have decided that the journey from Macinta is sufficient for one day." The priest refilled their cups from an earthenware pot: the coffee was strong and sharp. "I do not like to lose you, but I would recommend that you start for La Candela as soon as possible. In order that you are back again before dark—do you understand?" He swung a thin hand through ninety degrees. "It is not a place to travel without having daylight for company."

"On the volcano?"

"Out there. Anywhere out there. . . . Only yesterday there were bandits in Zacalocas. And last week—"

"Where's Zacalocas?"

"Over the ridge." The priest sipped the coffee. "Go now. Tonight we shall have our talk. I look forward to it. But while the sun is in the sky—"

He let a gesture finish for him. Lorrimer followed his advice and collected his camera. There were times when he had carried a gun, but this wasn't one of them. Except for the camera and a hip flask and a little food he took nothing.

He left the house and went through the village the way the priest had directed him—past the granary, across the *plaza*, past the church. The *plaza* wasn't deserted, as it had been the last time. Now it was thronged, a dozen mules and horses tethered by the fountain, trading in progress under the covered sidewalks—beans being bartered for tobacco, cloth for maize, spices and flyblown vegetables set out on mats, gaunt old men spinning twine or making wicker chairs, women with button-eyed children slung high on their backs. Sixty or seventy people must have been there. The alien white stone saints in their niches on the front of the church looked out over the stocky, slow-moving descendants of the conquered and colonized, and on the cobbled steps up to the studded west door the ritual and superstition of the copal-incense burners was already under way. In the high country, without doubt, there were more gods than one.

As soon as Lorrimer left the *plaza* he left the crowd. A few skinny boys pursued him with more determination than the rest, and he scattered some coins for them to fight over. Not satisfied, a couple waved their arms and shouted after him—"Dentist's woman . . . Dentist's woman"—their shrill cries chasing between adobe walls and sagging overhangs.

So what? Tomorrow he'd be gone.

The village came quickly to an end. Lorrimer skirted a cemetery, compact and crowded, no space between the clay tombs, crosses and carved emblems like a forest, a sense of desolation and abandonment over all. Better here, though, than at Auschwitz. Stemmle loomed in his mind, Kröhl turned dentist and medicine man, healer, pain-remover, Stemmle who was sinned against. . . .

Irony, like death, had no end.

He made his way out of the great saucerlike depression in which the village nestled. Birds scavenged among the crop patches. Here and there he saw people bent like reapers; once there was a well worked by a blindfolded horse; later a cart passed and the swarthy driver stared at him from beneath a broken high-domed hat as if he belonged to another species.

The sun was already drawing the sweat out of him. He wasn't going all the way to the crater. No one would ask for proof. He was going as short a distance as possible, and as soon as he found somewhere sufficiently remote which offered cover and protection from the sun he would lie up until it was time to return. From early on this had been his intention, and the sight of what lay ahead reinforced it.

From a distance La Candela had a magnificent symmetry, but at close quarters it had less appeal. Once Lorrimer came out of the depression the nature of the terrain quickly changed. It grew barren again, boulder-strewn, devoid of trees. Perhaps Navalosa was sheltered from the prevailing winds and drew its water from a natural fault in the strata. Whatever the reason, the slopes of the volcano were bleak and inhospitable, the exposed rock sometimes damaged like the surface of the moon, sometimes overgrown with splotches of wiry grass, the gradients all the time unrelenting.

After about **an** hour the village sank from sight. He climbed slowly. The sun had lost its identity in the blanched sky and the distances were hazed over, the horizon a lavender blue. He breathed hard in the thin air, humbled by the vastness of everything and the intensity of the silence, sweat running in greasy streams. Toward high noon he came across an area littered with huge boulders and decided to go no farther. The boulders seemed to vibrate in the heat. He picked on one ten times his size and settled in its shrunken shadow, plucking his shirt from his skin.

Around four he would start down. And when he got back, Stemmle should be there at last.

He slept, not meaning to but grateful when he woke that so much time had passed. "Men have died from time to time and worms have eaten them"—in sleep he remembered his father, white-haired and strangely angry, quoting Shakespeare when he told him about his visit to Auschwitz. "What did going there teach you that you didn't already know? That it doesn't pay to lose?"

It wasn't a dream so much as a moment relived. Granite, his father, quarried, not made. "Like father, like son"—there were times when Sarah couldn't keep it in.

Before he slept he had munched the tortillas the woman had given him and drank some pulque from his flask. Perhaps it was the pulque, viscous and acid-sweet, that had helped to put him under. Anyway, it was after three when he opened his eyes, and the shadows had shifted, leaving him half-exposed to the sun.

He got slowly to his feet. It had been premature to place the split chili against his gum that night, but how was he to know that Stemmle would keep him waiting? Yet, time apart, nothing had been lost. The cavity in the tooth was genuine enough and he'd at least been able to establish with reasonable plausibility that he needed treatment. In addition to which, as near as made no difference, the delay had given him the opportunity to demonstrate that his interest in La Candela was more than mere talk.

These things mattered. Anyone with Stemmle's past would wear distrust like a second skin. It was inevitable; he had survived so much. And, but for Riemeck, he would probably have continued to survive. Friend-of-a-friend Riemeck, Riemeck who'd shared with Kröhl the handshakes and the hurrahs and the merciless years of power, Riemeck for whom circumstances had now changed. . . . No one belonging to Europe could possibly arrive in Navalosa without Stemmle wanting to know why. And not only Europe—a white skin would be enough. It stood to reason.

There were no tracks, so Lorrimer didn't exactly retrace his steps. Soon after beginning his descent, he paused to take a succession of random shots of the volcano, simply in order that the camera should indicate it had been used. Most of the way his shadow was striding ahead of him like a giant. He jarred down, heavy on the leg, picking a route among scatterings of rock thrown up by the earth, the ground mostly wrinkled and iron-hard, in places brittle and flaking like a crust.

And not a sound except for him, no movement except for him.

Navalosa wasn't all that long coming into view. The sun was lower now, the light less harsh. By the time he had come off the swollen flanks of the volcano itself and had entered the cultivated depression around the village the sun was barely warm on his back: a few tinged strips of clouds were beginning to gather in the west. He was out of condition and his heels were sore. He came down into the village the way he had gone out, perhaps half an hour before dark, the dusk just about to thicken, and the priest called to him from outside the church as he passed.

"How was it at the crater? You got what you wanted? The pictures?"

"Fine."

"You made good time." The priest was slapping whitewash on the façade: two or three men were helping, high on rickety ladders. "No trouble?"

"None."

"You'll be pleased to hear the dentist is home."

"Ah . . . Thank you." Lorrimer's expression captured precisely the relief such news would give. "I'll clean up first, then go across."

He did exactly that. The woman let him in and he went to the place at the back where he stripped and bucketed water over his head, after which he came inside again and got into fresh underwear and a clean shirt. In the bit of mirror which had been placed beside the bed he examined his left lower front molar, just to be sure, then took a longish swig from the flask.

This time, he thought.

The woman was lighting the lamps as he let himself out. Left, then right, then right again—he wasn't dependent anymore. He came to the clearing where the house was and the frayed path led through the clumps of prickly pear. As best he could he came like a man who suffered just sufficiently to prefer mountain dentistry to continued discomfort. A number of gas cylinders were lying outside the door and the door was open. Lorrimer peered inside and saw to his surprise that several people were ahead of him—five or six, children included—squatting on the floor in yellow lamplight.

For a few seconds he hesitated, then he stooped and stepped into the remembered room. At first he couldn't see very well, but he was immediately aware of a sudden shrinking silence as the murmuring stopped and everyone turned to look at him. A lamp was hung head high in the center of the room and beyond its misshapen circle of light there was darkness. His gaze moved over those who stared so leadenly at him; then he peered into the gloom beyond them, where he knew the dentist's chair and drill contraption were. He was about to speak, more tense than he realized. But in the selfsame moment someone else spoke instead, someone invisible, someone with a dry rasp of a voice to whom Spanish was a foreign tongue.

"Quién es?" this someone asked impatiently. *"Estoy ocupado."*

Lorrimer's scalp seemed to tighten. And from a direction he wasn't expecting a wiry shadow of a man moved into his view.

Eight

Elsewhere he might have passed through the world unnoticed. But not here. Here everything about him was different—height, features, build, manner; only on paper was he a Guatemalan. This was Stemmle then, in string vest and shabby cotton work pants, with narrow head, beady eyes behind steel-rimmed spectacles, tallish and slightly stooped. All at once Lorrimer was confronted by him. The hair was gray and sparse, the face worn. Perhaps in daylight the surgery would show.

"You want me?" Only then did he stop. Until then he was moving forward, syringe in hand. "Ah," he said slowly, eyes traveling over Lorrimer from head to toe. "Ah, yes. I heard about you . . . Toothache, isn't it? You arrived from Macinta with the toothache."

"Yesterday."

A nod. "The priest informed me."

He went past Lorrimer to an Indian woman sitting with a snot-nosed child in her arms and gave her an injection, quickly, bending over. Strangely it was the child who whimpered, as if touched by some primeval fear.

"The priest informed me," Stemmle repeated. "On top of which you as good as left a calling card."

"I?"

"Indeed." He patted the woman on the shoulder and dismissed her with a gabble Lorrimer couldn't understand. "You certainly did."

Lorrimer countered cautiously, "How d'you mean?"

"You left a flight map behind. Is that how they name it? A flight map?"

"Flight map, yes." Lorrimer could have kicked himself; it must have fallen from his jacket. He said boldly, "I suppose I dropped it near the house when I was here the first time."

"Mercedes had it." If Stemmle was suspicious, he

masked his feelings well. Mercedes—so that was her name. . . . A frail goitered man stood up and opened his mouth close to the lamp. Stemmle angled his head and peered in. Preoccupied, he said: "I shall get her to give the map back to you."

"There's no need. I've no use for it anymore."

Stemmle kept the man standing and went out of range of the lamp. Lorrimer could hear him rummaging around somewhere in the corner of the room. The air was ammoniac with sweat, the matting filthy. A rat darted along the angle of wall and floor, but no one stirred, vermin a commonplace, stark existence the norm. Life itself was a kind of revenge.

"When were you last in a plane?"

Lorrimer lied. "About a month ago."

"Oh, yes?" Stemmle came back and gave a small bottle of brown fluid to the waiting man with a staccato burst of instructions. Then in Spanish, as before, he said to Lorrimer, "I hear you are English?"

"Right."

"In which case it is better we speak English." He indicated the remaining Indians and made the switch. "Privacy is always more satisfactory, don't you agree?"

"It's just as you wish."

"Do you understand German?"

"Only a very little."

"We stick with the English then." It was a quiet voice, despite the rasp. "Sometimes I have a chance to read but hardly ever for conversation, so you must forgive my mistakes."

"You speak well."

"Thank you."

Throughout this he had busied himself with another patient—a young boy—prodding flesh, feeling bones. Now he pressed an ear against the boy's rib cage and for the first time Lorrimer saw the flower tattoo on his left forearm—and the curious thing was that he took it for granted. This was Stemmle and Stemmle was Kröhl and in between he'd been someone else, and whatever merit there might be in what he did now could never eradicate the enormity of what he had done before. Some ghosts were never to be laid. This spare, gangling, myopic individual with a stubble of gray hairs poking from his chin and concave cheeks had been a monster.

"Where did you fly from?" Stemmle asked, offhand.

Lorrimer lied again, not quite answering. "I came down from New York."

"Oh, yes?"

"I'm preparing a feature on Guatemala's volcanoes."

"So I heard." Stemmle dispensed a handful of tablets to the boy. "Without the priest what would I know?"

In the time Lorrimer was with him this was almost the nearest Stemmle came to squeezing his face into a smile, but he was unconscious of any self-mockery.

"One thing he did not inform me of was your name."

Lorrimer told him.

"Whereabouts in England are you from, Mister Lorrimer? London?"

"Near London."

"And you're a photographer of volcanoes?"

"Until a month ago I'd never photographed a volcano in my life."

"But suddenly you start, is that it? Suddenly volcanoes are a sin of omission for you?"

He was attending a woman now, never still, never really looking at Lorrimer, yet probing, all the time probing. Despite his casual indifference he couldn't hide it. Already, depending on what was said, Lorrimer felt his mood could change.

"When you're a free-lance," Lorrimer replied, "you go where the money is."

"There is money in volcanoes?"

"After a fashion."

"Then Navalosa must be built on riches."

He sent the woman away with a pat and a push, then turned immediately to the person next in line. Some merely pointed to what troubled them—a torn foot, a swollen joint; others explained by way of question and answer. His treatments were rough and ready and stoically endured; only once, when a wound was cauterized, did anyone so much as grunt.

"As you see," Stemmle remarked, applying iodine with a feather, "I am not only a dentist."

"The woman at the priest's house told me what you do."

"They needed someone. Before I came there was nobody—not only in Navalosa but for long distances. San Camilo is meant to provide a periodic service, but what use is a visit twice a year? The high country is always the poor relation."

A beetle exploded against the lamp and spiraled down. Stemmle crushed it underfoot, bright red.

"This toothache of yours, Mister Lorrimer—when did it start?"

"Last week sometime."

"Suddenly?"

"Not really. I was in Guatemala City at the time, but it was only spasmodic and not at all bad, so I didn't do anything about it."

"In a few minutes I will see what can be done." Without warning he called, "Mercedes! Mercedes!" Within seconds there was the slap of sandals and the girl came into the soft fringes of the lamplight. "We have a visitor," Stemmle said in Spanish. "From England. Bring the tequila." The girl gave Lorrimer a studied sulky stare, then turned and left.

"*Not* my daughter," Stemmle said in a manner intended to dispose of every question. But an afterthought seemed to hold him and he asked, "Are you married, Mister Lorrimer?"

"I was."

"Not now?"

"Not anymore."

Sarah Lorrimer: out of sight, out of mind Sarah—even then; Sarah who'd one day said: "What's it like just living on the edges and feeling nothing inside? Dear Christ, what I'd give to see you at the mercy of your emotions for a change." Odd how the taunts lingered on when so much else had escaped.

Married? . . .

"Not for some years," he added.

Stemmle glanced at him sidelong. "They have a saying here—the past is somewhere someone else once made a journey."

Like hell, Lorrimer thought. But he kept his reply in context. "Once in a while, maybe."

"Always, Mister Lorrimer. Always."

Stemmle looked tired, his face bloodless. He finished with the last of those who waited, then wiped his hands on a piece of cloth. The girl Mercedes returned with the bottle and two enamel mugs and set them down. For a few moments she remained, ready to go, ready to stay, undecided as to her expression, her glances at Lorrimer as meaningless to another as an asterisk without a footnote.

"That's all," Stemmle said, dismissing her with a nod, and though she obeyed, her anger showed. "She believes in dreams, that one. For her they are a substitute for reality."

He took hold of the bottle with lean hairless hands and poured some tequila for them both.

"To your own dreams, Mister Lorrimer."

He said it with a twist of the lips. Then he fetched another lamp and turned the wick and lit it, after which he carried it to the part of the room where he did his dentistry, moving the other lamp there too. And while he did this he kept the conversation going.

"Did La Candela come up to expectations?"

"Pretty well."

"They say that some of the other craters are more dramatic. Would you agree?"

"I haven't covered all of them yet."

"Of those you have?" Stemmle insisted, offhand as ever.

Lorrimer stalled. "That's easier asked than answered."

"Have you been to Atitlán?"

"No."

"Tajumulco?"

"Not yet."

"Then you still have plenty of work remaining."

"It takes time."

"Of course." To Lorrimer's relief he changed tack. "Would you come and sit down, please?"

The chair was old, like a throne, its horsehair padding hard and uncomfortable. One of the legs was loose and the headrest was bound with twine. A clay bowl on the floor served as a spittoon. Stemmle went to the cabinet and took out the instruments he needed.

"Now," he said, approaching, eyes strained and intense. "Which is the tooth?"

Lorrimer pointed. The taste of antiseptic came off the mirror which was slid into his mouth and he hoped to God that Stemmle had some sort of talent with the drill; the first feel of the exploratory spike was blunt and clumsy. It was also strangely and unexpectedly disturbing to have Stemmle's arms around his neck. A slow squirm of a shiver passed over his skin.

"Ah, yes," Stemmle muttered presently. He poked around the cavity for a while. "When did you say this pain began?"

"Some days ago."

With a finger Stemmle hooked back the left side of Lorrimer's mouth. It was uncanny to be in contact. The warmth of his breath and the dry quiet rasp of his voice helped to push the mind in the direction of the obscenities for which he had been so efficiently responsible half a lifetime ago. By the hundred thousand those he had butchered would have heard this voice. Gassed, burned, shot, hanged, starved, tortured, terrorized—legions would have heard it. Whatever else about him had been changed the voice remained as it was.

"Your gum has been sore?"

"Yes."

"Why was that?"

"Why?"

"All along. . . . Like a scar."

"I don't know why."

"Didn't you notice it?"

"The soreness, yes. It's been very inflamed."

Stemmle drew away and returned to the cabinet. With his back to Lorrimer he asked, "How is the pain now?"

"It could be a lot better."

"Would you prefer I waited until morning? Lamplight isn't very satisfactory."

"I'd rather you did it today."

Stemmle jerked a nod. "Very well. More tequila first?"

"Is it going to be as bad as that?"

"I can't give you an injection. This is Navalosa, Mister Lorrimer."

Lorrimer grinned ruefully. He'd landed a story second to none and got his foot in the door for a bonanza, so he could hardly complain. He gazed hard at Stemmle, drinking him in. Everything about this man he wanted to remember. And this place. Everything.

"Shall I tell you something?" Stemmle made small talk as he fitted a drill head. "The chair I found in Quezaltenango, most of the rest in Guatemala City, a few odds and ends elsewhere. . . . The technique I learned from a book."

"Oh?"

"Does that worry you?"

With desperate cheerfulness Lorrimer said: "I'm sure you've had plenty of practice."

"Indeed," Stemmle countered. He worked the treadle with his foot and the drill made a whirring noise. "And you learn fast. Take heart, Mister Lorrimer. No one has died in this chair yet."

Nine

The slow-speed drilling jarred right through to the bone. Lorrimer sat stiffly in the chair, hands clenched, feet sometimes lifting, and gave himself up to it. By the time it was finished he had had all of enough.

"It could have been worse, yes?" Stemmle passed him a mug of water and he rinsed his mouth and spat into the clay bowl. "The drill heads are worn down. They no

longer bite the way they should . . . I am sorry." Stemmle
retreated to the cabinet where he began to mix the filling
cement. "The priest told me you would be eating with
him tonight."

"Correct."

"Use the other side of your mouth. Otherwise you will
be back with me in the morning."

"In the morning," Lorrimer said, "I leave for Macinta."

"On the way to another volcano?"

"Yes."

"Which one?"

"I'm not sure. It's an involved schedule."

The beady eyes looked slyly out of their corners at him.
He had expected suspicion, yet even so what Stemmle
then said came like a bombshell.

"Who sent you, Mister Lorrimer?"

"Sent me?"

"What really brought you here?"

"I don't understand."

His mind started running in all directions at once: until
then he thought he'd played it well. Stemmle came
toward him with the cement.

"This tooth of yours—the cavity was old, the inflam-
mation self-inflicted."

"Nonsense."

"Not in my opinion."

He bent over the chair from behind. Lorrimer attempted to restrain him.

"Hold it," he protested.

"It has to be done, Mister Lorrimer. Better to finish." Stemmle hooked his finger into the side of Lorrimer's mouth and began to pack the filling. A minute must have passed before Lorrimer was able to speak again, and it was long enough to sweat, to go in circles. But the urge to bluster spent itself and he took up where he'd left off.

"What the hell's on your mind?"

"I know enough about a person's mouth to be certain when I'm given false information."

" 'Who sent you?'—that's what you asked just now. Some crap like that."

"Yes."

"What in blazes has it got to do with the state of my mouth?"

"Look, Mister Lorrimer. Navalosa has forgotten the world and is forgotten by it. And then one day someone arrives and talks of toothache and volcanoes."

"So?"

"Someone without a toothache and with little knowledge of volcanoes."

"D'you think I took what you did with the drill just for fun?"

"Not fun, no."

"I don't understand you," Lorrimer said a second time. "How can anyone possibly—?"

"Give me the name of any of the volcanoes you say you have photographed."

Something rustled overhead in the thatch. "Why should I?"

"For one thing," Stemmle said tersely, "so that maybe I can stop thinking the worst about you."

"You're crazy," Lorrimer snapped.

The mirror found its way back into his mouth again. For a few seconds more Stemmle worked on the filling, packing, smoothing it over. His hands were shaking very slightly.

"Can you name a volcano, Mister Lorrimer? A single one?"

"My job's to follow a schedule. I'm a photographer, not a clerk."

"Not a journalist either?"

"Certainly not." He spat out some grains of cement. "Anyhow, what if I am? What's so special about you that a journalist should get you going?"

"Nothing's special about me, Mister Lorrimer."

"Except where you live. And how you live. And what you do. . . . You aren't exactly Mister Average Man, any more than this is the High Street."

"What I do is my own affair."

"Have I questioned that?"

"I don't know what you question, Mister Lorrimer. What I *do* know is that your reasons for coming to

Navalosa and needing my help seem to me"—he sought the word—"contrived."

"No more contrived, I dare say, than your own explanation for being here might seem to me."

Lorrimer had never imagined it would reach this stage. He stepped down from the chair and fumbled in his pocket.

"What do I owe you?"

He placed some notes on the cabinet. In the distance a horse whinnied, a shrill shaking sound somewhere in the night. And Lorrimer was suddenly uneasy, an unease that went beyond Stemmle and himself: all at once he seemed to experience another foretaste of alarm, of fear even, as inexplicable as before. Nothing to do with what was happening here. Already the lies were wearing thin, but lies alone, or the truth behind the lies, weren't enough to set him on edge.

"I don't want the money," Stemmle said.

"Keep it."

"I want instead to know who you are." He couldn't take his eyes off Lorrimer. "Who you are and why you are here—that is what I want."

"Didn't you believe the prospector either?"

"Prospector?"

"A prospector was in Navalosa at the end of the rainy season."

Stemmle frowned. "I am interested only in you." He

looked too frail for drama, yet there was steel in his voice.
"No one else."

"If it worries you so much, you must have something on
your conscience."

"Tell me."

"Don't press it."

Lorrimer moved across the room and Stemmle
followed. One of the lamps was smoking, blackening the
glass.

"Who sent you?" Stemmle tried once more, as persis-
tent as a moth at a flame.

"No one sent me. I came of my own accord."

"Why? For what reason?"

Lorrimer let it drop like a stone. "Because of thirty
years ago." It was ridiculous to pretend anymore.
"Because of Auschwitz and a man by the name of Kröhl.
. . . Because of you."

He thought the silence would never end. Neither he nor
Stemmle moved, Stemmle who for years must have
dreaded such a moment. Their eyes were locked. Out in
the darkness the horse whinnied again and the sound
seemed to finger Lorrimer's spine. Then Stemmle made a
small tossing movement with one hand, very telling, and
his shoulders shook as if he laughed. His face was a mask,
though, the eyes glittering behind the lenses. "You must
be off your head, Mister Lorrimer." He licked his lips.
"What name did you say?"

"You know damned well what name."

"But I don't, you see."

"Kröhl ... Lutz Kröhl. SS-Oberführer Kröhl."
Lorrimer waited a second or two. "Oh, come *on*," he
grated. "Why pretend? You aren't that good an actor."

"I'm not an actor, at all, Mister Lorrimer. On top of
which I don't know what you're talking about...
Auschwitz?" He acted as if he were shocked. "Who told
you such lies?"

"Who doesn't matter."

"To me it does."

"*What* I was told is what matters. And I got it loud and
clear."

"And wrong."

Stemmle stayed where he was, thin arms hanging
down. For the rest of his life Lorrimer was to remember
how he stood, quite rigid, outwardly quite calm, but God
knows what was racing in his brain. Once before, in
Bolivia, something like this must have happened.

"Wrong," he repeated. "Totally wrong."

Lorrimer shook his head. "What I got was as good as
fingerprints."

"Auschwitz?" Stemmle said with impressive bewilder-
ment. "Me?"

"More than just Auschwitz. Your dates at Auschwitz
and your function there. And the route you took when
you ducked and ran. And the surgery to your nose and
earlobes and lower jaw. And your marriage in La Paz,

Bolivia, when you used a different name. And how, when the woman died, you came here, ten years ago, with a flower tattooed on your left arm to obliterate the camp number you'd been wearing to substantiate your then cover story. . . . " Lorrimer paused, a long pause. "Tell me I'm wrong now."

The Adam's apple bounced in Stemmle's scraggy neck. With great control he said: "If I were this man, do you imagine I would live as openly as I do? I would bury myself, surely? Here I am known as far as the horizons. The German, they call me: *el Alemán*. Sometimes *el dentista*, sometimes *el curandero*, but always *el Alemán*. I make no secret of what I was born. If I were the man you speak of, how could I have lasted? And found respect?"

"You covered your tracks, that's how. And changed your face. And took a new name."

"There were no tracks to cover. I was never in Germany—never at any time in my life. I was born in this country. My parents were German. The proof is documented."

"Documents can be bought in the marketplace."

"I am a Guatemalan."

"Since when?"

"Since I chose. . . . You're wrong, Mister Lorrimer. You've been misled. What you are saying is ridiculous."

Lorrimer shook his head.

"Ridiculous," Stemmle persisted. "A criminal accusation."

"You know damn well it's not." A cockroach crawled between them like a clockwork toy. "If you're as lily white as you make out, why were you so anxious about me? 'Who sent you?'—God, you wouldn't let go."

"We are suspicious of strangers in the high country."

It was a lame reply, but Stemmle showed no sign of desperation. He flicked something from his face, the beady stare unflinching. The girl had entered the room, beyond range of the lamps, but he didn't see her. The rising clash of their voices must have brought her in.

"I don't know where you got your information, but I can only repeat—"

"I got the information from a friend. It doesn't only concern you."

Again Stemmle licked his lips. He said dismissively: "Memories last longer than friends."

"In your case I'm not surprised. What you don't seem to have grasped is that I'm talking about a friend—an ex-friend—of your own."

"What friend?" He blurted it out like a startled challenge. "What friend of mine?"

"Riemeck," Lorrimer said without delay. "Peter Riemeck."

A change came over Stemmle, a sort of crumbling. It didn't last long, and he mastered it, but it shook visibly through him. His mouth sagged and his hands moved in a curious jerking fashion. The girl stood dark and compact and silent in the corner, intrigued but excluded, and from

outside the house there were faint, ill-defined sounds—
perhaps like an animal being there, perhaps like someone
moving through the cactus clumps. But Stemmle was the
focal point: all the tension was inside the room. He
seemed to have to make an enormous effort before he
could trust himself to speak.

"I know of no one by the name of Riemeck."

"What else would you say?"

Nervously Stemmle snatched off his spectacles and
wiped the lenses. Without them his face seemed narrower,
his peering eyes more sunken. All the scorn had gone from
his voice; it was flat, leaden. "Who is this Riemeck supposed to be?"

Lorrimer had no time for rearguard actions. "He's put
it in writing, Stemmle. That's the only reason I'm here—
just to check. It seemed too good a story to be true. I just
wanted to be sure."

Stemmle fumbled the spectacles back on. And as he did
so, he was suddenly aware of the girl. He wheeled fiercely
on her.

"Go away . . . *Vete!*"

She didn't move. *"Qué pasa?"* she said stubbornly.
"What is happening?"

"Nothing . . . nothing."

She remained. She must never have seen him like
this—somehow at bay, somehow undermined—and dis-
dain showed itself like a wish fulfilled. But Stemmle forgot
her presence as quickly as he'd reacted to it.

"Please," he said to Lorrimer with great intensity. "You and I must talk. You have been fed with lies." He was frightened now, an old gray famished-looking man in a string vest and cotton work pants. "This name you mention, this one who gave you—"

"It's in writing, Stemmle. Riemeck's decided to cash in—and if I don't make use of it another will. And soon. There's nothing you can do about it. I'm only incidental." And anyhow, he nearly said, you're small fry; Riemeck promises bigger names than yours. But a kind of mercy prevailed. "You've had a long run, Stemmle, and it's nearly over."

Something brushed the overhang outside. The door creaked as it moved. They all spun around, Stemmle, too. As they did so a man entered with an urgent crablike shuffle, intending to take them unawares. And as fast as light the first thing they all saw about him was the gun.

"Cuál de ustedes el curandero?"

Ten

He was in black except for a blue neckcloth and a rawhide gun belt, everything dirt-stained, dust caked around his mouth and eyes, the eyes bloodshot in a heavy unshaven face. And one ear missing, just a hole. With heightened awareness Lorrimer took it all in, as well as the kind of gun, a revolver, like a .38. Except for the gun and the belt the bandit could have been a cattleman—cord trousers, leather jacket. Deep lines bracketed the cracked lips.

In Spanish he repeated: "Which of you is the *curandero?*" He used the gun as a pointer, first Lorrimer, then Stemmle. "You? . . . You?"

Stemmle seemed tongue-tied. "I am," he finally managed, back in his throat.

"There's someone outside needs help." The bandit went part of the way to the open door and whistled softly, like a pigeon calling. Then he looked them over, hostility in his flashing study of them. "Just the three of you here?"

Stemmle had another struggle for words, so Lorrimer answered. "Right."

"You'd better be correct."

"I am."

"Not only you. Each and every one, correct about everything." He made a small menacing movement with the gun. The lamps gave his skin a yellow tinge. Mexican, was he? Stocky, muscular, like a cat on his feet—no dispute about that. "Any militia in this village?"

"No."

"Police?"

"No."

"Any talk about us on the radio?" He got no answer and went on. "In connection with Zacalocas?" Still no answer. "A bank at Zacalosas—anything about that?"

"Something," Lorrimer said.

"What?"

"A mention, that's all."

The bandit grunted. He whistled again into the night

and simultaneously a second man came in. He was taller, this one, thinner, with a ragged mustache and a wide tan-colored hat. The left shoulder of his shirt was torn and brown with bloodstains.

"See to him," the first bandit ordered Stemmle. "He took a bullet yesterday. Clean him up."

The wounded man was hollow-cheeked, with a glazed-over wildness in the eyes. A pistol butt stuck over the top of drill trousers and the trousers were tied with string. He went to the dentist's chair and eased himself into it, the headrest tilting the hat forward over his face.

"I thirst," he said. "Bring something to drink—and quick."

Lorrimer glanced from one to the other, seeing them more clearly, initial shock and disbelief on the ebb. In a strained voice Stemmle turned to the girl and told her to boil water and fetch some pulque. The bandit with the drawn gun heeled the door shut.

"You," he said to her as she stopped between strides. "Don't leave the house. Go through the window, slip out the back way, and these two are dead—got it?" She said nothing and he didn't like that. "Got it?" he grated. *"Entiendes?"* And she nodded sharply.

"Sí, claro.' It would be madness to displease or disobey.

"Come and deal with my shoulder," the man in the chair demanded, unbuttoning his shirt. He had a voice like a frog, a sort of croak. "You've been hard to find, *curandero.* "

Stemmle crossed to the chair. His mind must have been in tatters, two worlds overlapping, two fears, Riemeck stalking like a ghost behind the nightmare reality of here and now.

"We looked for you in Jesús Pobre," the other bandit complained. "It was said you were there."

"So I was. Yesterday."

"Not when we wanted you."

He kept the gun drawn. The girl came back with a jug and poured the rancid-smelling pulque, taking it to each of the two men, who drank quickly and motioned for more. The one in the chair had dragged his shirt off: his sallow muscular body was no longer young, but not yet old. The bullet had scored a deep furrow across the very top of his shoulder, chipping bone on the way, and the opened flesh was swollen and blackened. He cursed when Stemmle touched it and struck the German in the chest.

"Careful!" he snarled. "I'm not a lousy Indian."

The bandit by the door pointed the gun at Lorrimer. "How does it happen there are two *extranjeros* under the one roof?"

"I had a toothache."

"You don't belong in Navalosa."

"No."

"So why are you here?" His gaze gave the impression that he was memorizing every detail of Lorrimer's features. "What brought someone like you to the high

110

country?" His mouth went out of shape. "Did you also try to take a bank and almost get taken instead?"

"No."

"We did, didn't we, Paco?" He had forgotten what he'd first asked Lorrimer. "Mother of God, it went wrong for us. From the first it all went wrong."

Now the girl returned, bringing a bowl of steaming water. She put it down on the cabinet by the chair. Her eyes met Lorrimer's as she passed him and they were big with fright, asking: What will happen?

"Who comes to this place?" the first bandit said to Stemmle across the pool of lamplight, but Stemmle didn't seem to hear. Chillingly, the bandit pressed the question. *"Curandero. . . .* Who comes to your house?"

"No one at this hour. Not unless there is sudden illness."

"Clean the wound and bind me up," the one named Paco growled. "That is the only treatment you give tonight."

He stiffened in the chair, teeth clenched and bared, as Stemmle went to work. The other bandit drank more of the pulque, careful not to lift his head too far, bloodshot stare restless and on the go.

"There is a horse to be watered—a lame and hungry horse."

"We have fodder at the back," Stemmle said in a dead, resigned tone.

"And we ourselves last fed in Jesús Pobre."

"Tortillas and beans. We have nothing else."

"What you have we eat."

The girl withdrew once more, the hint enough. The man in the chair yelped and twisted as Stemmle bathed and disinfected and dressed the wound. *"Ayeeee . . ."* he breathed. *"Ayeeee. . . ."* His companion pulled a stool to where he wanted it and squatted, jiggling the gun up and down as though he were estimating its weight.

"You," he said to Lorrimer. "You never answered my question."

Carefully: "Which was that?"

"Who are you and what are you doing here?"

"I'm a photographer." Out of the corner of his eyes he saw Stemmle glance at him sharply. "I came up from San Camilo and Macinta to take pictures of the crater."

"Why?"

"For a magazine."

The bandit snorted. "Did you hear that, Paco?"

"I heard."

It had amused him. "Where is the camera you use?"

"At the house of the priest."

"And where is the house of the priest?"

"Toward the *plaza.*"

The thin bandit left the chair, the wound bandaged, the arm dangling. The wide-brimmed hat was hanging on his shoulders from a strap across his throat.

"Watch them," the other one told him and he went

outside. They heard him going along the length of the house and then the horse being led around behind, the soft dust-cushioned sounds easily identifiable now they knew what was there. A few minutes elapsed before the bandit returned; he brought a saddle with him, a cheap studded saddle with a high pommel and stirrups slung across. On the other arm were a rifle and a pair of saddlebags made of a canvaslike cloth. He set the saddlebags down with care, but he didn't open them. The smell of the horse was in the cloth and leather.

Then he cocked his head almost conversationally. Matted ringlets of hair, mouth loose again. "How many in this village?"

"Including children?"

"Answer what I asked."

"Three hundred," Stemmle said. He was sweating thinly. Whatever else, he must have known how real the menace was. There was fear and there was terror, and they were very close to terror—all three of them. Dry in the mouth, Lorrimer had sensed it from the first and so, surely, despite his private state of shock, had Stemmle. Yet for a moment he seemed to forget how much he was putting at risk.

"I can do no more for the wound. What it needs now is time—and that we cannot provide, not like this, not indefinitely."

The bandits exchanged glances.

"We will feed you, yes." It could only have been nerves.

"And you can rest up for a while. But after that—"

"What are you telling us, *curandero?*" The one in black seemed fascinated. He walked toward Stemmle, hands loosely on hips. "What exactly is on your mind?"

"I'm saying that by morning you will have to be gone."

"Yes?"

"Only now, at night, for a few hours, are you safe in this house."

"Did you hear that, Paco? The *curandero* tells us what to do. And when and why."

"I heard."

Stemmle's head rocked with the blow, which came without warning and sent his spectacles flying. He staggered slightly, hands going up to protect himself from more. A bead of blood swelled in the corner of his lips.

"No one tells us what to do, *curandero*. Or when or why."

"Educate him," the one called Paco said. "Put him out of his ignorance. The photographer as well."

"Por qué no?" the other bandit agreed.

Just then the girl came with the beans and tortillas. It was as if he were seeing her for the first time, eyes on the bounce of her breasts beneath the blouse. He snatched a plate from her and began to stuff his mouth. She turned from him quickly, from the other man as well. Stemmle retrieved his spectacles and fingered his face. Lorrimer remained where he was, wire-taut, powerless, the rifle on the floor not even a temptation.

The food was wolfed down, nothing more said until

every scrap was finished. Silence was wrapped around the house, for miles around it seemed, isolating them. The village was less than a hundred meters away and yet, incredibly, nobody there knew what was happening. Two men and a cocked revolver had made this squalid room a separate deadly world.

"Paco says to educate you. So you have the right information, the right understanding of your situation. . . . So you don't get any more damn-fool ideas." The dark bandit fingered the hole of his ear and cleaned out his mouth with his tongue. "We got nothing at Zacalocas—that is the first thing for you to know. And the second is that what we failed to get in Zacalocas we shall get in Navalosa. . . . What do you say to that, *curandero?*"

"There is no bank in Navalosa."

"Who is talking about banks?" He waited fractionally, but Stemmle had learned his lesson. "People are more profitable than banks. Without people banks would not exist." The logic of it pleased him and he produced the same warped version of a smile. "How can I be wrong?" he said to Lorrimer. "You're a city man. Tell your *curandero* friend I make good sense."

"I don't understand."

"Show them, Paco, what we carry in the pouches."

The wounded bandit went to the saddlebags. From one of them he took a couple of sticks of explosive and laid them on the matting. A length of fuse followed, then some metal detonators.

"Have you experience of these things?"

"I know what they are." Lorrimer noded grimly.

"There is more. Not only what you see. More. . . . Sufficient to tear the heart out of Navalosa."

The bandit searched their faces for a response. In particular he addressed himself to Stemmle.

"Don't you care what happens?"

"I care."

"We have the power to kill this village. . . . It may not have a bank, but there is money. The people have money."

"Very little."

"Three hundred people?"

"You will find none poorer."

"When they learn what could become of their village they will remember where their money is."

Stemmle said nervously, "They have lost their village before. La Candela has seen to that." It must have cost him something to struggle on. "They will not easily—"

"La Candela did not offer them a choice. Not like us. It will be for the people to decide whether they prefer the one thing or the other."

There was quiet in the room, a quiet the bandit seemed to savor. He used it as a weapon, and it had the effect of dragging words off Lorrimer's tongue.

"You can't be serious."

"No?" the bandit said. He advanced with a sort of

swagger. "You think this is all a joke? Some kind of stupid joke, maybe?"

Lorrimer said, "You'll never make it on your own. There aren't enough of you to hold a gun to everybody's head."

God knows why he said it. They were face to face, and he half expected the butt of the .38 to his jaw. But, instead, the malevolent eyes creased at their corners.

"You sound like a tactician, *amigo*. Smart. . . . You see the difficulties. The people of Navalosa are going to need a little persuasion—yes? An incentive. Otherwise they might come to the wrong decision." He bared his teeth, gaze flicking from one to another. "What better incentive than the three of you?"

Eleven

Alarm prickled through the hair on Lorrimer's neck. It was the same when the horse had whinnied in the distance perhaps fifteen minutes ago, except that then he hadn't known why. And even now he only knew in part: terror was still at arm's length.

"Get the cord, Paco."

There must have been about fifty yards of it in one of the saddlebags, coiled in a loop as thick as a man's arm.

The tall bandit drew it out, then handed it to his companion with a gesture toward his bandaged shoulder.

"You," he said, and pulled his gun, taking over guard.

Their plans had been made before they ever gained entrance to the house—what they would do and who would do it; as the minutes slid away the more obvious this became. The girl was the first to have her wrists tied, Lorrimer next, Stemmle last. Once the cord was produced and the dark bandit ordered Mercedes to cross her hands behind her back there was an inevitability about what would follow—though only up to a point: the ultimate intention remained undisclosed.

The girl said in fear at the start: "What are you doing?" All she got by way of answer was a grunted "Wait and see." But then the bandit gripped her shoulders and spun her around with a leer and a laugh. "The dog has seen the rabbit, *guapa.*"

Not only were their hands tied; they were tied to one another, about a yard of cord separating them. When this was done they were left standing while the rest of the explosive was produced—twelve sticks in all. They watched the man make a bundle of the sticks; they were tobacco brown, granular, moist, in thin wax paper wrappings. The bandit's purpose hadn't dawned on any of them yet, but they saw how cautious he was.

"It sweats, Paco. It sweats a lot."

"Like the *curandero.*"

When the bundle was completed, he fitted the fuse end

into a detonator, crimped the detonator gingerly with his teeth until the fuse was held firm, placed a cluster of detonators around it, metal to metal, and buried the cluster deep in the bundle of explosive. And still none of them grasped his intention. He sat on his haunches while he did all this, but eventually he got to his feet.

"What time is it?"

"Eight," the man called Paco said.

"And we have the moon about when?"

"Toward ten. Half a moon only."

"You"—he jerked his head at the girl—"which is the nearest village?"

"Macinta," she answered in a low voice.

"How far?"

"Three hours."

The bandit whistled tunelessly between his teeth, toying with the fuse. It was every bit as long as the cord and looped the way the cord was, but stiffer, black against the cord's white.

"How far to the nearest telephones?"

"The same," the girl said.

"Nowhere nearer?"

"Se lo prometo." She shook her head. "Macinta is the first place with telephones."

"You'd better be right. For your own sake you'd better be a long way from lying."

He made a sign to the other bandit and went out of the room, taking one of the lamps. They heard him moving

121

here and there, followed by muttering and the clink of glass; quite soon he came back with a couple of bottles of pulque.

His companion eyed them with dissatisfaction. "No spirit? *El pulque es para los bichos.* It will be a long night. Cold."

"And we need to keep our senses."

He began loading the cloth saddlebags, the bottles into one, the fuse assembly into the other. Minutes had passed since Lorrimer, Stemmle, and Mercedes were roped together, and Stemmle was showing the strain most of all, as if he alone of the three of them had concluded how they were about to be used.

Yet he was the one who said: "What will happen to us?" He said it in a whisper, the way that others must once upon a time have asked the selfsame thing of him. And perhaps in asking he reminded himself of what he once was, and where, and with whom. Without warning he turned to Lorrimer. From the side of his mouth and in English, he pleaded: "For God's sake do not tell them who I am." And it was like the private surrender of his entire past.

The last thing Lorrimer could ever have believed was that chance would make them allies. And they needed allies now, all of them. The bandit straightened from the saddlebags.

"When you speak"—he glared at Stemmle—"speak so that Paco and I understand."

He stuck the barrel of the revolver under Stemmle's gray-stubbled chin, forcing him to lift it and look him in the face. There were close-ups in the war archives that recorded scenes like this; unconsciously Lorrimer noted the parallels.

And yet he heard himself: "Lay off him, can't you? He's old . . . tired. He's done you no harm."

"No lo creo!" the bandit exclaimed. "We have a child with us."

He picked up the saddlebags and hoisted them gently onto his shoulder, the one containing the explosive charge supported in the crook of his right arm. He glared at Stemmle again, seeing only the man he saw, distrustful only of what he didn't understand.

"It is up to you, *curandero.* You have a choice, just as the people of Navalosa are about to have a choice. In the *plaza* theirs will be, with the help of the priest. They will be able to choose between you and their money. Not houses, not buildings, but you—the three of you."

Stemmle's lips moved, but no word came.

The bandit said: "Time is short. But a charge of dynamite around your necks will encourage them to make up their minds."

"No!" the girl cried. She seemed to cringe. "No!"

"Speak to your friends in Navalosa, not to me. You will

soon have the opportunity. And if they are generous enough, neither Paco nor I will light the fuse."

They were herded into line, on each other's heels, Lorrimer between the girl and Stemmle. There was a terrible certainty about the bandits' intentions, menace sustained every time they spoke.

"Just a night walk through the village," the one in black said. "Paco alongside and me behind. And if anyone so much as makes a sound I will kill him." He yanked the door open. "No sound and no stopping—remember it with your lives."

After the lamplight the darkness seemed intense. They stumbled along the path between the thickets of prickly pear, their minds in turmoil, not knowing what to hope for, scared of a meeting on the way and the panic that might come of it, dreading what awaited them if they reached the *plaza* without incident.

"A joke, you think? Some kind of stupid joke?" Not then and not now. Christ, no.

They entered the village, crowding after Mercedes, kept close by the shortness of cord, eyes adjusting to a faint starlight sheen, and at first there was no one about except them. Voices came at them out of doorways, a few lights glowed, but they had the narrow zigzag streets entirely to themselves. Then near the *cantina* a couple of men stood talking together and one of them acknowledged Stemmle. For a dozen paces Lorrimer walked in dread of what might follow, wondering if the man had noticed they were bound. But the starlight was negligible and the moment passed. They went on, quiet as thieves, this way, then that, the labyrinth of alleys again deserted. A bitch on the prowl, some scampering children, a woman sluicing out a drain. . . . No one else; Navalosa was indoors.

The granary was next. Around its corner was the *plaza,* empty and star-green, and the bandit at the rear grunted when he saw it.

"Stop at the fountain," he ordered and they did so, without option, bumping into one another.

The girl pressed back against Lorrimer as if for protection; the swift passion they had shared seemed to belong to some other existence. Behind them Stemmle shivered in his string vest, feeling the night air's chill.

"Watch them, Paco," the bandit said and walked past the fountain, first to the steps of the church and then to the covered sidewalks where people came to buy and sell; it was dark now under the roofing. His boots gritted on the weed-cemented paving as he turned repeatedly, looking, thinking, making up his mind. After a while he paced out the distance between sidewalk and fountain. As he reached the fountain, they heard the grinding rattle of wheels, and almost at once a mule-drawn cart came into the *plaza* from around the side of the church.

"Sit," the bandit commanded, and they did as they were told, squatting on the fountain's parapet while he and his companion stood close, as if in conversation. Four people were in the cart, huddled figures impossible to decipher. Heads and eyes followed them. At Lorrimer's side a gun was cocked, the *click* sharpening the tension.

It was sickening to watch the cart pass, to be spared yet abandoned. When the *plaza* was once again deserted the bandit prodded the three of them to their feet and made them go with him to the sidewalk. There, in the ebony shadow, he roped them in a small circle, back to back, after which he took the explosive from the saddlebag and made a large noose of the fuse which he placed around their necks, the noose so fashioned that the charge dangled between them. While he did this he whistled through his teeth, unnervingly intent, as indifferent as if he were rigging dummies, and when he had finished they could each feel the weight of the explosive and smell its bittersweet stink.

Only once during several minutes of concentration did he open his mouth. Then it was to say to Lorrimer: "Better if Navalosa had a bank, eh?" A touch of lightness in the voice, exhilaration, adding a new dimension to their fears.

Presently the one called Paco said: "I fetch the priest?"

"Soon."

The bandit ordered them back to the fountain. "Move," he said curtly. They had to shuffle, the explosive swaying in the space between their shoulder blades. When they reached the fountain, they were tethered by a double twist of cord to one of the metal rings in the parapet to which pack animals were normally secured. Then the fuse was payed out and straightened along the ground until it stretched into the darkness of the sidewalk.

"Where is the priest's house, *curandero?*"

Stemmle answered woodenly, no defiance, the fuse across his throat like a garrote, the smell of the weeping explosive more demanding than gunpoint.

"Go, Paco. Get him."

The wounded bandit walked away. They soon lost sight of him in the starry darkness and then no longer heard his footfall. The sky seemed to shake with stars and Stemmle was shaking with them, teeth clenched.

"It is cold," he ventured. "I need a shirt . . . a coat."

"The more they pity you, the more they will pay."

The bandit had taken up a position near to where the fuse ended, but they couldn't see him. He was under cover with the rifle and the saddlebags, and when he spoke it was difficult to tell exactly where he was. The three of them stood tethered to the fountain, silent, numbed, imprisoned within themselves, inescapably aware that only a length of fuse and a man's whim separated them from oblivion. The weathered effigies on the front of the church looked down on them, and the silence in the *plaza* was so intense that it seemed to press in from the very ends of the earth.

Three hours to Macinta . . . Lorrimer strained to steel his mind and a remark of Sarah's seized its chance. "You're the pro, aren't you? You're the one who knows how to kill his emotions. . . ." He swallowed, dry as a bone, and shuffled his feet. Three hours to Macinta, six there and back, six hours the maximum Navalosa could remain isolated, the most their ordeal could last . . . It was an unimaginable length of time, impossible to contemplate. Already their nerves were at the mercy of every second.

The bandit hoicked in his throat and spat and the small wet echo of the sound fluttered about the *plaza*. Almost more terrifying than anything was the gambler's elation in his voice as he'd rigged the fuse assembly around their necks. He would use them to the hilt and squander them if need be. There would be no chance to plead if he panicked, no time.

"Let the girl go," Lorrimer called out. "Set her free."

"Don't tell me what to do, photographer."

Their bodies touched one another as they faced different ways. In the great quiet they could hear the wing-beat of a passing bird. Then, perhaps a minute later, they heard footsteps at the far end of the *plaza*—the priest's and the wounded bandit's, one quick and agitated, the other slow. The two figures gradually became distinguishable, the priest in the lead, the bandit close behind with his revolver drawn. The priest came hurrying toward

128

the fountain, peering in disbelief at what he was approaching, every step, every gesture, belonging to a man just roused and shocked out of sleep.

"Merciful Christ." He halted, appalled, stock-still. "What has been done to you?"

Twelve

Out of the darkness of the covered sidewalk the bandit said: *"Buenas noches, señor el párroco."*

The priest swung around, startled. "Who's there?"

"No one you know."

"I don't see you." He peered, bewildered. Whatever he'd been told at the house it wasn't enough. He used his hands, both together, like a bullfighter making a pass across his body. "What is happening to these people?"

"I shall explain."

"Why are they here?"

"I shall explain."

"Do as he says," the one called Paco grunted, "and don't ask questions."

"Listen, *padre*, and listen well. These friends of yours require your help."

"I don't understand." The priest turned as if in appeal to Stemmle and Lorrimer and the girl. The ropes he could probably see, but not the explosive or the fuse—not yet. "How long have you been like this?"

"Speak to me, *padre*, not to them."

"Who are you, for God's sake?" A little frantic now. "What do you want?"

"Money."

"Money?"

"A reward." He was polite to the priest. "Something for sparing them. Compensation."

"How much?"

"More than you could give us, *padre*."

"Say how much."

"As much as we would get from a bank."

They could hear the sharp indrawn hiss of the priest's breath.

Stemmle blurted: "They were at Zacalocas, these two. They're the ones."

"Shut your mouth, *curandero*."

"We have no bank in Navalosa," the priest protested, unaware of what had gone before.

"No bank, but three hundred people."

"That may be."

"From them we take the reward." The bandit's voice was blurred by an almost simultaneous echo. "From each and every one."

The priest clasped and unclasped his hands. "Who are you?" he demanded pointlessly again. It sounded stupid.

"If I answer that, it will cost you more."

"Already you expect the impossible. Three hundred of us there may be—"

"Don't preach at me, *padre*. Ring the bell."

"Now?"

"Now."

There was an awful finality about the priest's hesitant defiance. "It will do no good," he tried. "The poorest village in the whole of the high country—"

In the darkness of the sidewalk the bandit struck a match. Lorrimer stiffened instantly, felt the others stiffen with him, and saw the bandit flare with orange light, his leather jacket gleaming.

"Perhaps Paco didn't tell you, *padre.*"

"Tell me what?"

"Your friends have enough explosive between their shoulders to destroy the fountain they are roped to—and more besides. And the fuse to the explosive reaches to me here. . . . See—I have it in my hand."

The silence then was like a living thing, quivering, straining to endure. The match and the end of the fuse were about a foot apart, held up for them to see.

"*Madre de Dios,*" the priest whispered. Aghast, he watched the flame dwindle and die, the bandit vanish. "*Madre de Dios.*"

"You see, *padre?* You see why Paco and I have such confidence? The people of Navalosa are going to remember they have more money than they realized."

The priest took a pace or two forward, small jerky steps, all nerves and desperation. He spoke to the shadowy sidewalk, appalled.

"You cannot do this thing."

"If our luck had been better in Zacalocas, it would not have been necessary."

"The sin will be forever on your head."

"Words," the bandit said.

"More than words—and you know it."

"Preach at me again, *padre,* and you will have cause to regret. Your friends will suffer."

"They suffer as it is." The priest took another step, a little bolder. "For the love of Christ," he began to plead, "change your mind, change your heart."

"Paco," the bandit called, the inflection rising.

His companion swung the revolver-butt against the priest's neck, low down and slightly to one side. The priest sank to his knees and stayed there, swaying, clutching himself. He groaned, bent over.

"You were warned," the bandit said, politely even now. "It is regretted, but you heard me. Preach to the people of Navalosa, not to us."

The priest stumbled to his feet. For a long part of a minute he remained silent, hunched, watched by everyone, a thread of spittle hanging from his mouth. Over and above the pain he seemed to be struggling toward a decision with himself.

"These three"—he pointed, not done with yet—"let me stand in their place."

"No."

"Let me stand there with them."

"No."

"One does not belong to the village. And the *curandero* has been the salvation of many. And the girl, the young girl—"

"Ring the bell, *padre.*"

"And then?"

"Paco—show *el párroco* where the blankets are to be laid."

The wounded bandit nodded and walked to one side of the fountain. He tapped the broken paving with the toe of his boot. "Here," he said. "A blanket here, with a basket on it." Then he went halfway around the pool of the fountain, one hundred and eighty degrees. "Another here, also with a basket." He croaked as if his throat were raw.

From the sidewalk his companion said, "When the people come, *padre*, tell them what I tell you now. First, that if these three are to live, they have to be paid for. Second, that no one is to approach the sidewalk. Third, that only those with money are to come to the fountain

—and when they do they must come alone, never more than one at a time."

"It is a sin," the priest said bravely a last despairing time. "All this is a sin."

"You heard him, Paco?"

"I heard."

The starlight seemed to ebb and flow. The voices shook around the deserted *plaza* as if it were an empty room. Mercedes was lisping something to herself, Stemmle's teeth chattering, Lorrimer feeling the adrenaline drain.

"Ring the bell, *padre*. Loud and clear. But remember my instructions. Make sure they are known to everybody—and the consequences if they are disobeyed. Put muscle into every word."

"What happens when the money has been given?"

"Paco and I will decide if it is enough."

"And if it is not?"

"More must be found."

The priest clenched his hands. "You are animals."

He started toward the church. The way he angled his head showed he was still in pain. As he passed close to Stemmle, he stopped and pulled off the sweater he was wearing.

"No!"—like a razor slash from the sidewalk, politeness gone.

"The *curandero* shivers."

"No, I said."

The bandit fired as the words left his mouth. A foot

from where the priest had halted stone erupted from the rim of the fountain parapet and the bullet went sobbing into the night.

"Do what he tells you, *padre.*" Stemmle jerked.

"Next time I will shoot the girl. I promise you. When I say no, I mean no. When I say yes, I mean yes. Have I got to shoot the girl to make you believe me?"

"For Christ's sake do what he wants," Stemmle pressed again.

Under the stars the priest's face was like a mask, but his eyes glittered. He turned from them with a gesture of defeat and made his way around the fountain. The broken stone was fungus-white where the bullet had struck. The priest walked toward the church and mounted the steps. In front of the heavy studded doors he fumbled in his pocket for a key, then opened the wicket and stepped inside.

"Join me, Paco."

The wounded bandit moved briskly into the cover of the sidewalk. His eyes were on the bell in the open arch, yet before it moved someone had already entered the *plaza,* drawn, Lorrimer guessed, by the sound of the shot. A figure crossed the corner of his vision and stood perplexed and uncertain near the granary.

Then the bell began to clang, jarring the stillness. Lorrimer's pulse quickened. The person near the granary took a few paces, coming closer, but stopped suddenly and called out. Lorrimer didn't have to know the language to guess what was said—"What's happening?" or something like that. Stemmle and Mercedes would have understood but they made no answer. Again the man called out, alarm and curiosity mixed, and again drew no reply.

The bell heaved back and forth, screeching from disuse in its mounting, its deep reverberation shaking the air. The man near the granary was no longer alone; another had joined him. The stink of the explosive filled Lorrimer's nostrils, shredding his nerves a shade more. He peered across the *plaza* to the corner where the pair stood in baffled uncertainty, and even as he looked they were joined by a couple of others.

Six hours to Macinta and back—minutes from now someone was sure to set off, and the bandits knew it and would plan accordingly. But what if Navalosa also attempted its own rescue or simply refused to pay? Either possibility sent a swift breeze of fear gusting in Lorrimer's belly. There were dangers now he hadn't foreseen and the people beginning to enter the *plaza* underlined them. Their ignorance alarmed him, their curiosity, their very presence.

The bell stopped ringing as suddenly as it had begun. A murmuring took its place, a sibilant muttering. Between twenty and thirty people were in the *plaza* and more were coming all the time. In Spanish a woman cried: "*Curandero*—is it you? What are you doing there?" A young man jog-trotted forward, not too far, hesitant, bewildered as they all were by the sounding of the bell and the three of them standing by the fountain, speechless and back to back.

"Keep away!"

The priest emerged through the wicket-door.

"Keep away and listen to me!"

The muttering rose to a crescendo. The priest raised his hands in appeal, advancing to the edge of the steps, and as he did so the rim of the moon lifted over the roofing of the sidewalk where the bandits were.

"Listen," he cried. He paused momentarily, waiting for the murmuring to quiet. "Some of you fetch the others. Everyone has to be present, the whole of Navalosa."

"Por qué?" Several voices took it up. *"Por qué, padre?"*

"Because there are bandits with us—*pistoleros*—and they demand it."

The crowd buzzed, a different sound.

"Where? Where?"

"There. In the darkness of the sidewalk."

Silence came sharply, alarm with it.

"Some of you go fetch the others," the priest shouted again. "Quickly, quickly . . . I beg you. It is a matter of life and death."

A few turned and hurried off. Others were still arriving, pressing against those already there, beginning to form a ragged semicircle about forty paces from the fountain. Everyone was turned toward the sidewalk where the bandits waited, invisible under cover.

"Keep away from the fountain," the priest shouted,

"and keep away from that sidewalk. And listen to me as you have never listened before. For the love of God, listen!"

The moon was edging up, silvering the *plaza*.

"The *curandero* and the girl Mercedes and the photographer who came to La Candela have a charge of dynamite hanging from their necks." A noise like a leaf-rustle filled the *plaza,* shocked and abrupt and brittle. "Unless we obey, the bandits will light the fuse. Unless we do as they tell us, these three will die. . . . Do you hear me? Do you understand?" He took their murmuring for assent. "Listen then—and remember that we are all at the mercy of these men. We have no choice. A terrible thing has suddenly happened to us all."

Lorrimer craned his neck, eyeing the leathery moonlit faces, the girl's fingers reaching for his, the sweaty whiff of Stemmle's fear compounded with the stench of explosive.

"The *pistoleros* demand money . . . money from everyone in Navalosa. Only if we give enough, will these three be spared."

The priest paused. Into the pause there came from the sidewalk like a threat the snap of a rifle-bolt being thudded home. And the crowd shifted, backed away.

Thirteen

"Two blankets are required. Two blankets and two baskets."

The priest came down the worn steps of the church. Late arrivals were entering the *plaza*, massing with the hundred or so already present. The priest indicated where the blankets were to be spread, walking hurriedly from one place to the other as if demonstrating some special ritual.

Here, he said. And here.

"Someone fetch these things."

Nobody made a move. The lack of response angered him. He wheeled on those who were nearest, voice thick with emotion.

"Is it my wish, do you think? The dynamite is as good as round my neck as well." He pointed at a woman in the front of the crowd, naming her, shaming her into going. "What if your own man was tied to the fountain like a beast? Would you not bring some blankets then?"

Everybody was edging a little farther away, moving to one side of the *plaza*, fear like a contagion, beginning to spread. The woman turned and scurried off.

"What the *pistoleros* threaten is an atrocity. We alone can prevent it, you and I together. . . . A little money, something from all of us."

The priest went back up the steps to be better seen. He swayed, not recovered yet, a weakness taking him in the legs. Perhaps half of Navalosa was there by now, and a murmur swept them.

"When we give what we shall give, we have to do so one at a time. Is that understood? One at a time."

Somebody—a man—called hoarsely: "Not all of us have money, *padre.*"

"I know how it is."

"There are those who cannot give."

"I know how it is," the priest repeated bitterly. "But these are the demands, and they have to be met."

"How?" Not the same man, but others. "How?"

"Ask yourselves."

"That is no answer."

"Answer it yourselves then. Look at these people and answer it yourselves. Release them from their terror."

He suddenly launched into prayer, very brief, very passionate, half a moon shining down, the air crisp and cold. Lorrimer and Stemmle and Mercedes stood tight against each other, shoulders touching, the past forgotten, Auschwitz forgotten, Riemeck and the manuscript forgotten, yesterday in the house and what happened there only a couple of hours ago gone dead in their thoughts.

"Come on," Stemmle gritted, jaws clenched. "Come on. . . ."

The girl whispered: "Will they kill us?"

Lorrimer: "It's a bluff."

"They will if they don't get what they want." She was beside herself.

"No. . . . No." ·

But they would. The pressure of the fuse across his throat seemed to send his mind beyond conscious usefulness. He watched a woman return with the blankets; her companion was carrying two baskets. Both women were timid, both constantly looking toward the priest as if for encouragement. Together they spread the blankets on the paving where the priest had directed, a basket centered on each one.

"Tell everybody once again, *señor el párroco*. Remind

them. We are not here for the good of our health."

The cruel, confident, lazy voice could have come from almost anywhere along the covered sidewalk. The one called Paco chuckled, and the crowd stirred, seeing neither.

"What can I say," the priest called out, "that I have not said before?"

He descended the steps slowly, in pain still. He went to within a pace of one of the blankets and tossed a silver coin into the basket; it glinted as it spun through the air.

"For you, *curandero*. For you, Mercedes. For you, *señor*." His gesture was as dramatic as his words, not meant for them alone. "Do not despair. All will be well." He had immense dignity. Then he spread his hands. "Friends . . . friends," he began but managed no more, choked with distress and his own suffering.

Silence settled over the *plaza,* brief but intense. Soon a man shifted forward to where the other blanket was and pitched a coin. Incredibly, a few people were still arriving, but only the very old and the very young were absent. As soon as the first man had started back to his place, another followed his example, then a woman, three women in succession, then a man again. At first, there was a sense of urgency: those who gave approaching in quick succession, going to left or right of the fountain as it suited them. Mostly the men tossed the coins, whereas the women stepped onto the blankets and dropped their money into the baskets. But the initial eagerness wasn't long sustained. Shortly there were minutes of waiting when nobody disengaged himself from the crowd.

"So soon?" the priest cried. "Would you offend the God who made you? Where is your pity?"

Others came. Few of the coins were silver pieces. Sometimes they fell short or rolled off the striped blankets and lodged in the cracks between the paving slabs. Lorrimer quickly lost count of how many had given, just as he was losing track of time, but among the first dozen or so was the bat-faced woman from the house of the priest. The cord bit into his wrists and his hands grew heavy with blood. Already, he told himself, someone would have started for Macinta. *Must* have. He stared at the moon-blur of faces across the width of the *plaza*, unclear in his mind why the thought should give him cause to hope when, with absolute clarity, he could see that a strong-arm party from Macinta would find itself as powerless as everybody in Navalosa.

One of the bandits cleared his throat. As the moon climbed, so the sloe-black shadows hid them all the more. A marksman would never be able to pick them off, yet their simultaneous destruction was the only guarantee that the fuse wouldn't be ignited. Until dawn the bandits were secure—and dawn seemed a lifetime away. They'd have bled Navalosa white by then. Either that or—

"Consider what the *curandero* has done for us," the priest urged hoarsely from the steps.

A man ventured forward and spilled a rain of small

coins direct into a basket. Then a girl came, wrapped against the night, hugging herself as she backed away. In the front of the crowd Lorrimer made out a couple of ragged youths who'd yesterday taunted him—"Dentist's woman . . . Dentist's woman." But yesterday no longer seemed in any way real, none of it. Now the youths were merely two more strangers with a stake in his life.

"Where is the silver?" the bandit shouted. "Anything less than silver is trash."

Stemmle's teeth kept chattering. Once or twice he muttered to himself in German. On another sudden tide of panic Mercedes breathed: "They will never get enough."

"It's early yet."

"Madre de Dios—"

"Easy," Lorrimer said, fingers hooked around hers. "Easy."

Now when a coin fell into the baskets, there was a layer of money there to greet it; the clink of metal began to punctuate the silence. Individuals advanced and withdrew as before, impassive, no clue to their private feelings.

"Preach to them some more, *padre.*"

The one called Paco laughed. "It is good to give. Good for the soul." The quick-thrown echo of his ugly voice scampered around the *plaza.* "Remind them."

The priest gestured helplessly.

"Either you remind them or you will bring the altar candlesticks from the church."

"To do so would be sacrilege."

"Words," the invisible bandit said and spat.

The crowd swayed. The priest began to plead with them again, speaking of love, mercy, duty—these three—and everything he said was charged with desperation. A few more people separately made their way to the blankets, a coin here, a coin there, pitiful contributions. Oh, Christ, Lorrimer thought. His hands were going numb and it was beginning to seem as if there had never been a time when he hadn't teetered on the brink of terror. Stemmle shifted his legs and the explosive charge swayed between the three of them, tapping their backs. He felt another stream of sweat pump out of him.

How long would it take the fuse to burn? Twenty seconds? Thirty?

"The *curandero* is renowned throughout the high country, but he chooses to live in Navalosa. We are the beneficiaries. There is hardly a person here who is not in his debt. Show your gratitude therefore. Share what is happening, accept what it costs. . . ."

Each fresh appeal by the priest brought a response, but the gaps when no one moved and the crowd waited were increasing. An hour must have passed, an hour at least, the longest Lorrimer had ever known, and the baskets didn't appear to be full. Several scores of people must have given already and the blankets were littered with coins, but only a fool could have hoped the bandits might be satisfied.

Fluid gurgled as a bottle tilted. "Not enough, *padre.*"

"We are not rich in this village. I have told you—"

"There's not enough."

The priest came down the steps a second time, loosening his watch from his wrist. "See," he cried and held it aloft. "No one grieves for what can be replaced." He trod amid the scattered money and parted with the watch, desperate to set an example. "Who gives now lends to God."

"Who asked for cast-off scrap?"

The priest straightened, courageous as ever. "People cannot give what they do not possess."

"You know the terms." The voice was vicious. "Where are the silver coins?"

"Silver is already on the blankets, in the baskets. You expect the imposs—"

The shots were as fast and sharp as the double crack of a bullwhip. Two stabs of flame in the darkness of the sidewalk, two spouts of water from the pool of the fountain, the beginnings of a gasp from the crowd—all in the space of a second. The gasp lengthened, spent itself. And as it died, so people started to run, scattering, something snapped in them, out of control.

In vain the priest shouted. They emptied out of the *plaza*, past the granary, past the church. Only a few stood their ground.

"Come back! Come back, d'you hear?"

He was wasting his breath. He started after them, grabbing at those he could catch, but they shook him off.

Dust lifted into the moonlight until it was like shot silk. A kind of wail rose from the alleys around the *plaza*, a moaning, panic in the sound.

"God," Mercedes jabbered, "God, oh God, oh God."

The cold air couldn't hold the dust. It settled fast and they saw what there was to be seen again. Blinking, Lorrimer counted seven people who'd remained. Seven and the priest—they were spaced about the sudden emptiness of the *plaza*, and one of them, the bat-faced woman, was on her knees.

The priest turned in anger to the sidewalk. "You see what you have done?" It was the voice of a man accusing partners of a misjudgment. "They would have given, allowed time. Yes. . . . Another hour and you would have been satisfied."

"Who says?"

"From now on it will be harder. . . . They are like children."

"Paco and me decide when we're satisfied. Nobody else."

Stemmle coughed. His face had a fever-wet sheen of fear, yet his body shivered. "There is money in my house."

"Fetch it, *padre.*"

"Beneath my bed." Stemmle coughed again. "A metal box." The explosive swayed as before, slapping against their shoulder blades; the smell of it wafted up. In a voice unnaturally thick and stifled Stemmle shouted: "I cannot stand much more."

"You heard, Paco?"

"I heard." Again the answering chuckle, frayed by its own tight echo. "We have a comedian out there . . . *Un cómico.*"

The first of those who had remained in the *plaza* made a move. A small bowlegged man walked defiantly to the nearest blanket and flipped his contribution onto the rest. Another followed—and the glint showed the single coin to be silver. Then the woman rose to her feet and darted forward, sobbing, subsiding onto the church steps.

"Get the people back, *padre*. And be sure they don't come empty-handed." One of the bandits was urinating against the wall; they could hear him. *"Plata es lo que plata vale."*

The priest began to cross the *plaza*, hurrying, at his wits' end.

"What about you, photographer? We forgot about you. All this way from the city streets—you will have money."

"Some."

"Paper money?"

"Some."

"If the *curandero* gives, then so should you." Lorrimer could picture the mocking dirt-stained mouth and the veined eyes. "Is that not a reasonable thing to expect?"

"I have money," he gritted.

"At the house?"

"On me."

The urinating ended. Feet shuffled. "Take it from him, Paco, while he remains in one piece."

Fourteen

The wounded bandit came out from under cover. He came fast, taking advantage of the emptiness of the *plaza* and the absence of possible risk. He made straight for Lorrimer, the wide-brimmed hat slung behind his neck like a disk. A yard away he shoved the gun into the top of his trousers. With his good hand he started through Lorrimer's pockets, and the search didn't take long. From the hip pocket on the right side he pulled a fold of notes, and when he saw what they were, he whistled.

Over his shoulder he called: "The photographer carries a small bank of his own."

"Good for him."

"Mexican dollars."

"We should have been photographers, Paco."

"Look where it gets you, and the company you keep." His mouth twisted. He returned to the shadows of the sidewalk, treading lightly, restless. "I tell you we could have used the tequila."

"Never celebrate too soon."

Of the seven people who had stayed behind only one now remained. The others left the *plaza* once they had given, taking to their heels or slinking off as if their nerves had finally broken or they couldn't bear to be witnesses anymore. But the housekeeper woman was still there, kneeling on the wide steps of the church, and the gabbled murmur of her prayers went on and on.

A solitary cloud dragged over the moon and the *plaza* darkened. Lorrimer's guts seemed to shrink as the sense of isolation intensified. He pressed against Stemmle and Mercedes, shoulder to shoulder, needing them. They were cramped and desiccated—and he needed them in a way he'd never needed anyone, every whirling thought in his head centered on the chances of survival. A time was coming when Navalosa would yield no more, when night began to run out; one or the other. What then?

Stemmle's teeth rattled. He whispered, "Midnight, isn't it?"

"God knows."

"It's got to be . . . got to be."

The *plaza* seemed to expand as the cloud pulled away from the moon. The housekeeper hadn't moved—jabber, jabber, as if in delirium.

"Shut your mouth," the bandit growled. She paid no heed and he bawled at her. "Shut your mouth, *mujer,* or I'll shut it for you."

This time she obeyed, but she stayed where she was. A sound came from the darkness of the sidewalk. It could have been the scrape of a boot, but in the instant of its happening they all three took it to be a match and went rigid simultaneously, fear draining down into their thighs, imagination on the rampage. Then the reaction hit them, the awful inner trembling, the ice and fire sweat. And as the seconds passed, they heard the clatter of approaching footsteps.

The priest led half a dozen men into view from behind the granary. They kept close to one another, and the priest walked with his arms spread as high as his hips in a gesture of protection. Halfway across the *plaza,* he halted them.

"I have your box, *curandero.*"

Stemmle was silent, but the bandit said: "Place it on the blanket."

The priest advanced alone, the metal box in his right hand; everyone could see it now, and it was small.

"Call that a box?"

"There is no other," Stemmle answered.

"We thought you were making a worthwhile contribution."

"It is all I have." Stemmle suddenly seemed possessed by rage. "All I have," he screamed in Spanish. And then in German, *"Das ist alles was ich habe."* He stamped his feet. *"Alles!"*

He staggered slightly and Lorrimer and Mercedes staggered with him. The echo of his voice spent itself around the *plaza,* silence waiting everywhere like a giant holding its breath. The priest froze between strides during Stemmle's outburst, but then he went to the first of the blankets and put the box beside the basket. As he retraced his steps, the bandit threatened him once again, threatened them all.

"No more insults, *padre.* No more single coins. One more bit of trash and the giver invites disaster."

The look on the priest's face was one of hatred. "Mother of Christ," the bat-faced housekeeper whispered to herself, "pray for us. . . ." The first of those who had come with the priest went forward at his signal. He was an old man, skinny and white-haired, hollows in his cheeks and shadows in his eyes where the moonlight did not fall. He stepped onto the blanket to the left of the fountain, the way most women did, and unclenched his fist. A shoal of silver spilled through the air. A grunt of approval came from the sidewalk.

"Not before time. . . . Not before time, *padre.*"

High above the church roof a compact pattern of lights was plowing southward through the star-quiver. Faintly, very faintly, Lorrimer could hear the throb of engines. The priest also saw and heard; most of them did, and a moment of envy possessed Lorrimer's mind, stronger even than fear, an enormous envy for the ordinariness of other people's lives, their freedom, security, comfort. The real world was somewhere else.

Stemmle staggered again, Stemmle who so short a time ago had pleaded: "For God's sake, don't tell them who I am." And Lorrimer shook his head as a dog shakes water from itself, close to retching from the madness that had overtaken him.

What pressures the priest had brought to bear he could only imagine, but money poured onto the blankets, each of the newcomers as generous as the last. The six men parted with as much in five minutes as had been given in the previous hour, and when they had finished, the priest went away to find others. And he found them, and brought them, sometimes in twos and threes, sometimes singly, and watched as they relinquished what was theirs.

One man tossed a small bag of coins on top of the rest and said: "I have no more either, *curandero.*" There was a kind of heartbreak in the solemn voice. Nobody else said anything, but after a while the wounded bandit chuckled and called out: "They value you, after all. How does it feel to be appreciated?"

The shock had gone out of those the priest escorted back, but they were still scared, still nervous as they made the lonely walk toward the fountain, outrage and bitter hurt somehow compounded in their bearing. Some of the women wept as they scattered their savings. "Everything you possess," the priest must have urged those he went to. "Nothing less than all you have. And then your prayers." It must have been something of the sort because the baskets overflowed and person after person fell to his knees after he had given. Some crossed to the church steps, some retreated and knelt at random about the *plaza*—twenty-five or more already there and others still coming.

"Aren't you satisfied?" Stemmle shouted blindly at the sidewalk. "Isn't this enough for you yet?"

There was no answer. A spasm shook him, the fuse vibrating against their necks.

"You are breaking these people. They will curse and hate you as long—"

"You talk too much, old man."

"Bastards. . . . Bastards, the pair of you."

"For Christ's sake!" Lorrimer hissed. "What are you trying to do?"

The night was absolutely still and the moonlight was like a lacquer. For perhaps the hundredth time Lorrimer and the girl glanced sidelong at each other, no veneers, fear as blatant now as lust had been yesterday. Every so

often their fingers touched and held on. Words needed
hope to be worthwhile, whereas physical contact trans-
ferred whatever strength remained between them. And
hope, at best, was on a razor's edge: even with the ransom
heaped in front of them, there was no telling how the
nightmare would end.

Lorrimer guessed wildly at the hour. At the far corners
of the *plaza* the alleys were blocked with those afraid to
venture nearer. At intervals the priest pushed through
them, coming and going, bringing whoever he had
privately managed to persuade. The intervals were longer
than they had been at first, and the numbers diminished
rapidly, but the giving still went on.

"More yet, *padre.*"

God above.

Stemmle had brought the ransom in. He was in a bad
way now, shivering uncontrollably, lurching about as if
his legs were near to collapse. All the sacrifices were on his
account. Incredibly, if they got out of this alive, Stemmle
would have been the reason.

Stemmle . . . Kröhl . . . Lorrimer's strained mind
couldn't rise to it.

The money had buried the baskets and he wondered
dully how the bandits would get it away; there was far
more than the saddlebags could carry. He shut his eyes,
traveling down into himself, but found no refuge. His
hands were bloated, throbbing with pain, and whenever
Stemmle staggered or swayed the tug on the cord came,

and he yelped and the three of them lurched like drunks together.

One o'clock? Two? Time had lost all shape. The bandits spoke to each other.

"We should take the candlesticks from the church."

"And put a curse on ourselves?"

"They would fetch a fine price," the one called Paco persisted.

"Forget it."

"We were cursed in Zacalocas. We had our bad luck there."

"The candlesticks would bring more. . . . Forget it," his companion said again, sharper. "Once and for all, forget it."

He was the leader, this one, the one in black with the blue neckcloth and the hole for an ear; he made the decisions. There was a gurgle as a bottle was raised, but no sign of him, no sign of either, only the fuse stretching into the darkness of the shadow, and that was threat enough. Another person came to give, a woman, a cloth wrapped around her shoulders and a domed hat on her head, plaits hanging down. She threw money on the pile, and some of the coins went wide and spun on their rims.

"Señor el párocco!"

The priest was in the *plaza.* "What is it?"

"We want food. Food and drink for traveling."

Mercedes caught her breath, Lorrimer too, and

Stemmle froze—all in that instant. An end was on its way, at last.

"And something else."

"Yes?"

"The money is to be split into two loads, each load to be in two halves, two bags joined by an arm's length of rope. Is that understood?"

"Claro."

"The making of the loads to be done here, by the fountain."

"Claro." The priest swung on those who knelt nearby. "Which of you will help? You heard the *pistolero*. Who will help with the making of the loads?"

There was no reluctance now, no holding back. People offered themselves without reserve, relief in their voices, eagerness. The woman from the house of the priest rose from her knees and ran toward the granary, the priest calling after her and the woman nodding as she ran. Others crisscrossed the *plaza,* converged on the blankets and the hillocks of coin.

"Two loads, each in two halves," the priest reminded them. They had been robbed of the money and must suffer its loss; but soon they would lose the bandits too and the long terror would be over. This alone mattered. He gazed at Stemmle and the girl and Lorrimer and saw what the night had done to them. "Soon," he said to them quietly, as if no one else was there. "Soon now." He turned briskly toward the covered sidewalk and addressed the opaqueness where the bandits were, anxious to speed them on their way, to have them gone and no one killed, to be able to offer up thanks.

"Your horse is lame."

"So?"

"We will exchange it for another. And provide you with a mule."

"You heard that, Paco?"

"I heard."

"You are generous, *padre*," The bandit spat. "But you forget. If we wanted another horse, we would take one. A dozen horses and a dozen mules and we would take them. That is how it would be."

"I don't understand." The priest shifted uncomfortably. "Your own horse has broken down."

"We will not be riding."

"But the money . . . There is coin by the kilo."

"Where we are going no horse or mule could travel."

The priest shrugged. "How—?" he began, and Lorrimer suddenly had a forward flash of what was coming. He quailed, alarm clenching like a fist in his stomach. "How," the priest continued, "will you carry so much?"

"With help."

The priest hesitated, a glimmer of truth dawning. Oh, God, Lorrimer thought.

"Whose help?"

"We take the same three with us."

Fifteen

All movement in the *plaza* came to a halt: the stillness was like a wind gone down. Stemmle slumped and the girl Mercedes moaned.

"Listen," the priest said shakily, "listen—"

"Don't tempt me, *padre.*"

"These three have suffered enough. More than enough." He wrung his hands. "Ride," he pleaded. "Take horses and a mule. Take the best we have, but do not use these people anymore."

"You are wasting our time."

"There are passes to the west and north, good tracks, good gradients. I promise there will be no pursuit."

"Get the bags made, *padre*. Have the food and drink prepared. Enough for five, enough to last beyond tomorrow."

"But—"

"We leave within the hour."

"The *curandero* is weak. The photographer has no experience of the high country. The girl would soon be a burden to you." In despair the priest attempted cunning. "You are being unwise."

"Is that so?"

"In my opinion." He paused, half in the hope of a reply. "As sure as God made Jesus Christ I think so. . . . To go without horses would be lunacy."

"Yes?"

"Yes." Speaking at the block of shadows and saying: "Yes. Without doubt."

"We are mad then. Does that satisfy you?"

Distraught, the priest moved from one foot to the other. "Why do you want these three?"

"Because," the bandit said.

"Because?"

"You talk too much," the one called Paco snarled. "All night your tongue's been flapping and I hate the sound."

Feebly, Stemmle cried: "How far are we to go?"

"You shut up as well."

The priest turned his back on the sidewalk. Mercy was a word, pity a word; guns and explosives made him powerless. He gestured hopelessly to everybody in the *plaza,* and they continued what they were doing, hating it, shock and dismay expressed in their slowness. The priest walked straight up to Stemmle, stopped a pace or two in front of him and again dragged off his own sweater. Then he held it aloft and, facing away from the bandits, addressed them. "Would you shoot the girl?"

No answer.

"You said you would shoot the girl if I gave the *curandero* this."

"Why chance it then?"

"You have squeezed this village dry. To give a man something against the cold will cost you nothing now."

"Drop what you're holding onto the blankets."

"Can he not wear it?"

"Later."

"Why not now?"

"Don't press your luck, *padre. Lo siento mucho.* No one goes near that explosive except us."

The money was pushed into four heaps, the bags were made from gunnysacking, the food and drink was brought. Then the bags were filled with coins until each was roughly the same weight, after which the bags were tied at their necks and roped in pairs. All this took time, twice as long as it should have, the people involved coming and going, the priest their overseer, unease and bitterness in their hushed murmuring. The whole of Navalosa had been cheated. At one point the canvas saddlebags were tossed from the sidewalk into the moonlight, and the woman from the house of the priest packed them with food.

Presently the bandit said: "When I tell you, *padre*, you will cut them free from the fountain."

"And then?"

"The three of them will move to the same place as the loads."

One of the pair worked the rifle bolt, its hard sharp thud a deliberate warning.

"No tricks." He was speaking to everyone now, not using the priest as a mouthpiece anymore. *"Señor el párroco* has been full of praise for the *curandero*, so you cannot wish to have him dead. Have you not paid to keep him and the others alive?"

Stemmle strained toward Lorrimer. "Where will they take us? Where d'you reckon—"

"The frontier?"

". . . never, never make it."

"No tricks," the bandit warned loudly again. "Cut them loose, *padre.*"

The priest took a knife from one of the women who had sewn the bags and severed the cord close to the metal ring in the fountain's parapet. Then he started shifting the loads over to the sidewalk, setting them down beside the line of the fuse; on the last trip he carried the sweater. The bandits must have been very close when he was near the sidewalk, but he didn't peer into the shadow for them, didn't look up. He was beaten, finally beaten, and it showed. When he had finished, he returned to the area of the fountain. For a moment he struggled to speak but failed, words useless. Wretched and defeated, he flapped his hands against his sides and looked away.

"Over here," the bandit called. "Move."

The three of them shuffled stiffly across the *plaza*, awkward as crabs, the explosive like a clapper between their backs, the feel and smell of it still terrifying. At the sidewalk's edge they stopped, but the bandit told them to go farther, under the roofing and into the shadow. They obeyed, stumbling, and were blind at once.

"Paco has the rifle and his reflexes are as quick as light."

The bandit's tone was almost conversational. He lifted the loop of fuse from around their necks, reaching between them to do so, and they began to make him out as their vision adjusted. Their hands remained bound and they were still tied together, but the explosive was taken away and terror diminished until it was only fear again.

The bandit crouched in a deep squat and dismembered the charge, separating fuse and detonators, doing it expertly yet quickly. All the while they saw him a little more clearly, his wounded companion as well, Paco, while in the moonlit stillness of the *plaza* half the village waited in silence, the priest standing all alone.

Stemmle shivered violently, whereas Mercedes was as rigid as stone. God knows what the time was, but they had been hours together and Lorrimer felt sick enough to vomit, and weak with the feeling, no strength to spare for anyone else.

The bandit straightened and came to them again. First he slashed the cord that joined them together, then the binding to their wrists, and for a while they didn't seem to realize they were free. Nervously they held themselves, massaged their swollen hands, put them to their dry lips and blew.

Lorrimer was prodded. "You and the *curandero* will take the money. And you, *guapa*"—this was to Mercedes—"carry the saddlebags."

None of them said anything. The bandit stepped out into the moonlight and retrieved the priest's sweater. He tossed it to Stemmle who struggled to get it on, grunting, crude in the sounds he made.

"We go in the order we came."

"Which direction?" Lorrimer said thickly.

"As if we travel north."

The frontier was north. So perhaps his guess had been right. But forty to fifty kilometers. . . . And what happened if they were driven that far? What happened then? *Afterward?*

The bandit lifted the loads into the shadow of the sidewalk. "Pick them up," he ordered.

The money was heavier than Lorrimer had reckoned

on. He slung the bags over his shoulder, delayed reaction beating in flurries against his senses. Heel and toe the bandit wheeled on the *plaza* and began to shout a final warning, but Lorrimer deafened himself to the voice and the threats it was making. He'd been hollowed out, made gutless and afraid, and no matter what happened nothing could ever be the same again. That much he knew already, though how it would be different, what would be different, he couldn't yet grasp.

He stared at the stocky, stolid Indian people of Navalosa and their priest, all motionless in the silver-green *plaza*.

"We go now," the bandit shouted, the one in black leather, never more dangerous than when he was being polite. *"Gracias, padre . . . Gracias, todo el mundo."*

And Paco chuckled that awful voice: "Get started. On your way."

Mercedes led. Lorrimer was on her heels and Stemmle behind him, one bandit at the rear, the other at Lorrimer's side. They went along the length of the sidewalk and entered the alley in the lee of the church. A buzzing of voices was released behind them and the priest cried in a final admission of defeat: "We shall pray. All the time we shall pray."

"See?" the bandit said. "What it is to have friends."

They made a turn, hemmed in, pale glimmers of light showing in squat houses but no one to be seen, no one following, no one in wait, the threats taken to heart.

"The candlesticks would have been a gift."

"We did all right without them, didn't we?"

They were very sure of themselves, elated yet watchful, eyes everywhere. And they kept close, a revolver at arm's length from Stemmle's spine, the rifle pointing sidelong at Lorrimer. Their feet scuffled the dust, all of them, and the only other sound was the rasp of Stemmle's breathing. Mercedes had the saddlebags like a halter around her neck, but Lorrimer and Stemmle both carried their deadweight loads slung back and front across one shoulder.

Two more turns. "Which way you taking us, *guapa?*"

"You wanted north," the girl said.

It was a long time since she had spoken. The village began to break up; there were open spaces between the houses and outlying shacks. Already it was a way Lorrimer had never been before; La Candela was in the opposite direction. Once, as they brushed an overhang of thatch, he suddenly heard whispering and another time, for the briefest of moments, he thought he glimpsed someone peering from a doorway. But this was all, and with every step, every turn, whatever chance there was of rescue diminished.

The alley changed to a path across wasteland, then skirted a communal refuse tip. Now that they were clear of habitation the moonlight seemed to have lost its intensity; out here everything was grayer, distances deceptive. The path became a track and the wounded bandit took over in the lead, the other one staying behind Stemmle, the explosives carried underarm in a wrapping of blanket. Lorrimer stumbled and the coins clashed together in the gunnysacking bags. He felt terribly limp, incapable of trying to brace himself in readiness to plan or act. If there had been a chance to save themselves, it was while they were under the sidewalk roofing and their hands were first freed. They might have tried something then—gone for the guns, broken away, scattered. Just for a moment the chance had been there if only they had risked it together; he saw it now. But hindsight was a fraud. All too well he knew that when it mattered they were stunned beyond reasoning, beyond collaboration, beyond action.

The track led out of the depression in which Navalosa grew its crops. It climbed and dipped and climbed again, the high country crumpled on all sides, immense, empty, and ghostly quiet. After about a mile the village had vanished. When Lorrimer looked back it was nowhere to be seen, and he felt their isolation as never before.

He repeated Stemmle's question, nagged by it. "How far are we going?"

"Until it suits us."

"And then?"

"We shall have finished with you."

"What's that supposed to mean?"

"You'll be no use anymore, that's what it means."

Cat and mouse answers, unnerving, a sort of exhilaration in the voice again. Lorrimer clenched his teeth and kept in line, following Mercedes, Stemmle close behind. The weight of his load was beginning to tell and the thin night air was cold on his sweat. Horses would have made short work of what they'd so far covered, but after about an hour the bandit who led abandoned the track and headed cross-country, the ground at once uneven and tangled with chaparral, no trees, nothing above waist height.

Ahead there were ridges rearing up to the stars; that was where no horse could go. They came on an ankle-twisting descent across the face of a vast slope, Lorrimer breathing hard now, out of condition. At the base of the slope the bandits ordered them to rest and gave them water from canteens in the saddlebags the girl was carrying. Her load was the lightest of the three, but in any case she moved with the steady rhythm of someone who belonged to the uplands, better than either Stemmle or Lorrimer. Stemmle suffered the most, limping already, showing his years and what the night had cost him. When they threw themselves down, the girl sprawled close to Lorrimer, not speaking yet inquiring with each glance whether they were going to be all right, a gloss on her blue-black hair and the look of a child in the frightened way she huddled into herself.

Twice more they moved on and twice more they stopped—the last time for sleep. They were exhausted by then, raw-eyed, the loads like lead, the ropes cutting into their flesh. Dawn couldn't be far off, but Lorrimer's mind wouldn't stretch to it, wouldn't reason, wouldn't cope with any more. They had reached a defile at the foot of the barrier ridge, boulders and gritty dust and resonant walls of rock, and his legs were giving way.

"Take an hour, Paco. . . . Turn and turn about."

"Okay."

This much he clearly heard. But he lost consciousness the moment he hit the ground.

Sixteen

He was never far under, twitching sometimes the way a dog does. A sound finally brought him up from the shallows with a jerk and a grunt which he heard as his eyes opened. It was daylight, burning bright, and he ached in every muscle, a chill in his bones. He stared blearily about him, seconds passing as the sickening truth sank in and he remembered where he was. And who he was with, and why.

The bandit in black was propped against a rock, cleaning the rifle. His scruff of beard was days old. He grinned at Lorrimer. "Did you dream it was a dream, photographer?"

Lorrimer moistened his lips. The wounded bandit lay in a patch of shade, his good arm across his face, the saddlebags nearby and a bottle of pulque sticking from one of the pouches. Lorrimer had never seen him in daylight before, neither of them, not even Stemmle. Lamplight, starlight, moonlight—but never like this. Only the girl and he had shared the light of day, back in the room where the magazine pictures were pinned to the wall. A nightmare ago. Now she was curled at his side, within reach, whereas Stemmle was yards away, in a heap, as if he'd tripped while on the run and gone down and had his spectacles fall from his face.

In a low voice Lorrimer said: "What time is it?" In the night his watch had stopped.

The bandit shrugged. "How can it matter to you?"

Bad teeth in the cruel mouth, the blue neckcloth stained with grease, a gold stud in the only earlobe. The rifle was a Springfield .30, the stock battered and gone dark with wear.

"How can it matter to you?" the bandit repeated.

Carefully Lorrimer said: "Everything matters. What day it is. What time it is. Where you're taking us matters."

"Guess."

"The border?" *La frontera.*

"Wrong."

"Where then?"

Cat and mouse again, enjoying it. "What is bad about the country we are in? Navalosa gave us plenty. Borders are for those who've failed."

"Where then?"

"Where the military does not go." The bandit jerked a thumb over his shoulder. "Into the mountains. Through the mountains. Out the other side." He spaced the sentences. West: they were heading west, twice as far as the border. "The hard way, photographer, the safe way."

Their voices roused the others. Each woke in different fashion—the one called Paco snatching for his gun; Mercedes, wide-eyed and staring; Stemmle, lost without his spectacles, mouth open until he'd found and fumbled them back on. They were silent for a while, all of them, coming to terms with reality, taking it in, tension resurrecting. Then the wounded bandit began to chuckle, softly at first, in bursts, growing louder, head back, teeth bared, the defile echoing the chuckle until it sounded like madness. Nobody moved, exchanging glances. The chuckle spent itself and the bandit shook his head.

"That priest. *Hombre, hombre,* we had him out of his mind." His eyes leaked from the thought of it. "No bank ever worked so hard."

"Or took so long . . . Get the food, Paco."

Some of what the women had put together was shared among them—corncobs and tortillas. The tortillas were dry, but the corn buds chewed up soft and mushy. And there was water, a long mouthful each, the canteen passed around.

What day was it? Saturday?

The sun was low in an empty sky but coming to burn and blister. The bandits spoke between themselves, then ordered everybody to their feet. The best time to move was now, now and at evening.

"On your way."

At once the weight of the bags of coin dug into the soreness on their shoulders. Within minutes it felt as if there had been no respite from it, no sleep, nothing but this. They went in the same order as before, weary from the outset, their minds in a stupor. They followed the defile until the bandit in the lead chose to climb. He zigzagged up to the broken backbone of a ridge, and they went with him, dumb and desperate, without choice. In the defile it was shadowy and still cool, but on the slopes and on the ridge itself the sweat began to pour and sting. There were peaks in the distance, other ridges in between, ravines separating them, the colors gray and barren-brown and sage-green. Nowhere was there any trail. They were moving across the hard grain of the land, and sometimes the bandits read the ground as if it were a map, sometimes instinctively, but always they read it well.

At the first of the morning's halts, the one called Paco growled: "We should have gotten ourselves tobacco in Navalosa. Ayee, what I would give to smoke."

"Forty-eight hours and you can smoke all you want."
His companion looked at Stemmle, knowing his words
were measured. "We go west, *curandero*. Beyond the
mountains there are villages. And beyond the villages are
the big towns and the sea."

"What becomes of us?"

A lizard ran in a cleft of rock: there would always be
life. "Perhaps we turn you loose."

"When?"

"Perhaps, old man," the bandit said, and the other one
laughed, a wildness in his eyes that the hours of night had
hidden from them.

They made another start. Muscles were jumping in
Lorrimer's back and he labored, with his face screwed
against the glare. In the narrow high-walled ravines the
air lay hot and stagnant, but out of them the vibrant
glassy glitter was blinding, sapping their strength.
Whenever they slowed or hesitated the bandits urged
them on, but already Stemmle seemed past responding.
He was one-paced, stubborn with fatigue and the leaden
weight of the money. He hugged the sacks to himself and
moved with a dull fixed stare, for all the world like a
refugee clutching a precious item of salvage.

Lorrimer's brain seemed to be emptying itself of controlled thought. The sun inched up and their own
shadows dwindled. The sky grew discolored and took on a
brassy glare.

Tomorrow was Sunday and tomorrow he was to have

been in Mexico City. "After Sunday, Mister Lorrimer, we will go elsewhere"—vaguely he remembered the voice, the face, the beginning of his reason for being here. But the thought of tomorrow was like make-believe. Survival was the gnawing obsession, somehow getting out of this alive.

Stemmle would never help him, not the way he was. Nor could the girl. . . . So how? How? Panic was never far away. When they next halted and collapsed, he found himself staring at his captors with sullen hatred.

"Stop looking at me!"

Sweat pricked Lorrimer's eyes. The bandit in black dissolved, vanished, reappeared.

"Cut it out, d'you hear?"

The strain was on them all. They reached a bulbous cliff face, perhaps forty feet high, and the bandits conferred for a while—whether to scale it or whether to work along and around. In the end they chose to climb and the one in black went first while the other squatted with the long barrel of the Springfield across his thighs and covered them. A length of cord was tossed down and the loads hauled up. Then they followed, clumsily, no strength in their holds. The rock was pitted and cracked like pumice and threw its heat at them, but each in turn completed the climb and started to walk again, chafed skin rubbing raw.

By noon they were high on a saddleback with a gorge in front of them and another ridge beyond. The sides of the gorge were as steep as a V, and everywhere they dug their heels small avalanches went cascading down. Lorrimer moved his tongue around his mouth, searching for saliva. It was getting so that no sooner did his thoughts knit raggedly together than they fell apart again, leaving him more scared than before, trying to regather the broken strands, certain they were important and that when he got them all of a piece there would be something he knew he could do—something rather than blunder endlessly toward the mountains piled against the sky.

Water flowed in the bottom of the V during the rainy season, but there was none there now. They picked a way along the parched trough, dragging their blistered feet, shifting the loads. After a while they climbed again, dust caked on their skin, the dribbling avalanches renewed, the ground brittle and crusted. At the top of the gorge they rested once more, the wounded bandit with the wide-brimmed hat the only one to have shade.

After drinking from the canteen he studied the girl's recumbent body, white wedges of muck in the corners of his eyes. For a long private while he studied the shape of her, then looked across at his companion.

"Yes?" was all he said, a single croak.

"Why not?" Then: "There'll be a time."

No more than that, the first words for at least an hour, but enough to alert the mind. Mercedes might not have been there, none of them. But she had felt the stare, heard the exchange that singled her out, and her lips trembled. On an impulse Lorrimer reached over and gripped her shoulder. Stemmle watched in a glazed sort of way, oblivious and indifferent, apparently unaware that whatever was going to happen to them was already decided. The girl pressed her face against Lorrimer's knuckles, smearing the grime, and despair possessed him as never before.

The heat was savage, scalding; it dried Lorrimer's sweat as it came and burned through the soles of his lacerated shoes. The bandits herded them on, coolies, cattle—"Move! All of you move!" How far they'd traveled he couldn't imagine. Hours, all run together, all fused and made indistinguishable by pain and effort and dread. "The hard way, photographer. . . ." They straggled like prisoners from a battlefield, their legs sometimes out of control, sending them off-balance into crazy corrective dances. Several times Stemmle fell. For a while they trudged across a high table of wind-compacted ash, ribbed like a whale's belly and sprouting tufts of coarse grass. The ridges and peaks ahead of them gathered shape and gradually disclosed their detail. For long periods there was often no sound except the drag of their feet; then perhaps one of the bandits would curse or stagger like the rest of them.

Immersed in his own bodily torments though he was, Lorrimer noticed the way the bandits were weakening —and drew a kind of strength from it. Buzzards circled, riding the undercurrents. The shadows were lengthening and a haze had begun to powder the lavender distances, but the loads were murderous and inescapable. They climbed once more, desperately slowly, the mountain barrier creased like elephant's hide, stained and forbidding. Stemmle wasn't the only one to fall. The bandit in black also went down, and he took his time about getting up, eyes slashed with pain as he nursed an ankle.

Increasingly after that, when they halted and lay panting, he was as spent as any of them, slobbering water from the canteen. Lorrimer watched him through a blood-red throbbing, watched the other one too, watched everybody. What he was hoping for he didn't know. Without a gun he was useless, and even with a gun he'd be suicidally slow when they were lightning quick. Getting to a gun was wishful thinking anyhow.

And yet, and yet. . . . Hope remained a craving and wouldn't let go.

The girl always flung herself beside him when they rested now. Stemmle had diminished for her; even in her exhaustion she made it blatantly clear. And Stemmle seemed beyond caring. This time he had collapsed within arm's length of Lorrimer, first onto his knees and then onto his hip and shoulder, keeling over like a felled tree; there was a soggy crunch of metal as he hit the ground and dust lifted around him. Lorrimer spared him a glance, moving his swollen tongue about the leathery confines of his mouth. Waves of dizziness blurred his vision and his lungs burned. Then his own eyes closed and he escaped into what darkness there was, the smell of gunnysacking in his nostrils and the thudding of his heart like that of something trapped.

Minutes passed. One of the bandits was retching dryly. The air was absolutely still, but dirt suddenly pattered against Lorrimer's cheek. He was barely aware of it, going under, sinking fast. Then the same thing happened again, twice more, an insistent granular flip across the eyes. He opened them with a start and found himself staring at the flower tattoo on Stemmle's forearm and a bent finger triggered in the surface dirt. Beyond both was Stemmle's haggard face. And to his astonishment he realized that the feebleness had gone out of the expression.

With an amazed lift of hope, he watched Stemmle's lips start to shape their silent message.

"They . . . will . . . kill . . . us."

"I . . . know."

"We . . . must . . . kill . . . them . . . first."

Lorrimer swallowed, a green bile rising in his throat. "I know," he mouthed back.

Seventeen

Neither moved an inch. But Lorrimer shivered, swept by a kind of delirium, tension and disbelief combined. Desperation shared was like hope fulfilled. Incredibly, all this time, Stemmle had faked his condition. Night long, day long, his frailty had been a calculated sham; suddenly it was clear. Lorrimer gazed at the gray flecks in the beard-stubble and the lined sweat-glazed face a yard away from his own. For hours he'd assumed that his nerve and strength were practically gone.

"How?"

"I . . . have . . . a knife."

Stemmle's eyes indicated where it was—the right leg, low down, on the outside of his calf most likely, strapped into position. And it must have been there all along, before yesterday, since God knows when, a permanency, part of the survival kit. So much was flicking through Lorrimer's mind in a fantastically fast haphazard way that he took a couple of deep heaving breaths in an effort to find some calm.

He was looking at a professional survivor, an expert; he had to remind himself. This was Kröhl, ex-SS-Oberführer Kröhl, who knew more about survival than most. The eyes now meeting Lorrimer's were sick with strain, yet behind the feverish bloodshot look they were tough and resourceful, just as behind the beard-stubble there were the scars of special surgery.

Stemmle. Kröhl. . . . Everything about him was a deception. And Lorrimer thanked his stars for it, trembling as his thoughts ran wild. All at once it had come about that Stemmle might give them a chance to save themselves, Stemmle of all people.

Sweat salted his cuts and grazes; his entire body seemed to be stinging. Stemmle's lips began to move again, and Lorrimer tried to read their slow exaggerated message.

"When . . . there . . . is—"

One of the bandits scraped to his feet and Stemmle's eyes shut instantly. The bandit went around a rock to relieve himself. Stemmle's lids fluttered but didn't open. Lorrimer waited, still not moving, like a log. The sun was being sucked low into the west and the shadows were stretching all the time. He lay on his side with his back to the girl and with Stemmle's right hand still folded in the dust in front of him. Fear was always quicker than the power to reason, yet reason reaffirmed what he already knew; the girl would be raped and all of them killed when they'd served their purpose.

And now Stemmle could be their savior. . . . It had come to that.

The bandit Paco slouched back into view, then sank down until he was obscured by Stemmle's body. And Stemmle opened his beady penetrating eyes. He knew about killing, all there was to know.

"Not . . . yet."

"How . . . long?"

The minutest of shrugs was part of the answer. Lorrimer watched the cracked lips but couldn't get the rest. He frowned, wire-taut.

"Must . . . wait," Stemmle told him. "After . . . dark."

Lorrimer's gaze strayed to where the knife was concealed. Hope went out of him for a moment, and all he could imagine was disaster. One knife against three guns. How? he thought and flinched, squeamish in spite of everything, the green bile still in his throat.

The wounded bandit swore and got up again and took the saddlebags from where the girl had put them.

"Let's eat," he said to his companion. He unwrapped the wad of tortillas, all dry and hard now. "You?"

"How's the water?"

"Half a canteen. That and some pulque."

"Lay off the pulque."

Their voices were hoarse, the exchanges slow. A tortilla was tossed from one to the other. Lorrimer pushed himself onto an elbow and looked at them. The rifle was on the ground, the revolvers stuck into the tops of their trousers: weakness was making them careless.

"What you want, photographer?"

"Some of the food."

"Take it."

Lorrimer rose unsteadily and stepped over the girl. It was easy to get close to the bandits if there was a reason for it. What would Stemmle's be? And at night, too? He bent and peeled tortillas off the wad for the three of them, picking up the canteen as well.

"Easy with that. This time tomorrow you'll still be needing it."

Lorrimer turned his back on them. He gave a thick tortilla to Mercedes, squatting beside her as she took a swig from the canteen. She rinsed the water around her mouth for a longish time before she swallowed, eyes searching his for strength, reassurance, a different world from his in every look she gave him and the way she endured.

"The German's got a knife." The urge was to tell her, but he could not, dared not.

Stemmle hadn't stirred. Lorrimer touched him and he made as if he jerked awake, vacant-looking behind the grimy steel-rimmed lenses.

In English, sounding confused, he said: "They will take turns at sleeping."

"Right."

"I'll wait for the one with the wound."

They got away with the exchange and Stemmle drank from the canteen. His resilience still astounded Lorrimer, who drank from the canteen himself. It was going to happen. He felt his pulse quicken. They were talking about something which could have them dead by midnight. Or free. And it would happen. He swallowed the mouthful of flat warm water and returned the canteen to its place between the bandits; there were salt rings on their clothing where the sweat had dried. He went back to the others and lay down and chewed the flap of baked maize, famished yet hardly able to cope with the way the food stuck in his throat.

The light was thickening, losing its harshness. The mountains ahead of them were claret-colored, with folds like a draped cloak.

Stemmle spoke again in English, pretending to ramble.

"I will lose my spectacles," he said. "A chance may come out of that."

Anxiously, like someone found out, Lorrimer glanced at the bandits. The bandit in black was looking directly at him, his stare very dark and shining but indifferent, dead at the center. The other one warned: "Shut your mouth."

Stemmle risked another sentence: "Could be hours yet."

"Shut it, d'you hear?"

The heat of the day was still in the ground. The five of them lay in attitudes of abandon, silent, chewing, deep in their own desperations. When Stemmle lost his spectacles—what kind of chance? And what was he, Lorrimer, expected to do, if and when it came? And what if Stemmle losing his spectacles produced nothing? What then? . . . There were questions galore and he couldn't answer them. Life or death was on its way, and they were too closely watched to manage even a few seconds alone to work something out—details, alternatives. For Lorrimer this was the worst of all worlds, knowing a little but not enough, not nearly enough, tension slow-coiling like a spring.

He had gone beyond the reach of irony. It didn't matter about Stemmle anymore. Kröhl-that-was was now their savior-to-be, and only the method mattered, nothing else. He would be frantic by the time the moment came and everything was suddenly instinctive, the body reacting before the mind. The Springfield was the gun to go for;

already he'd decided this. Whatever Stemmle did, the rifle was the thing to get his hands on. Somehow.

A squirm moved through him. Oh, Christ, he thought. He'd written about these things. Afterward. They happened to other people.

Stemmle was showing no further interest in making contact. Perhaps he was waiting for dusk. Several times Lorrimer tried to catch his eye, but in vain; the dazed enfeebled look that Stemmle had adopted was almost too effective, difficult to disbelieve.

Hours yet. . . . The sun had touched the mountains and dusk would be swift, but not much else was certain.

"Mercedes?"

A minute before she had been awake but not anymore. Without knowledge of the knife, it would have been easy to go under. Exhaustion was dragging at them all; in particular the bandit in black seemed close to the limits of consciousness. The rifle was beside him, a hand's breath away, and everything could happen quicker than it took to blink. Yet he'd slowed a lot. The ruthless confidence in and around the *plaza,* the mocking courtesy of his treatment of the priest—both might have come from another man.

"*Señor el párroco . . .*" Years seemed to have passed through Lorrimer's brain since Navalosa. Vaguely he supposed the story would be on the radio by now, just like the Zacalocas report, but there wasn't any comfort in the thought. Rescue had never been a likelihood. First the night had swallowed them up, and then the mountains. They could have chosen any one of a thousand ways to go.

The wounded bandit settled against a slope of rock. "You want a couple of hours?" he croaked at his companion.

"How about you?"

"I'll manage." He pulled the revolver from out of the string around his trousers. "Take them while they're on offer."

Stemmle glanced slyly at Lorrimer, a slitted look, lid-heavy. He would make his move early, within the next two hours; this much had been decided for them.

The day burned itself out in a blaze of crimson and gold. Everywhere the distances were shrinking fast. The mountains turned to cutouts, black against the sky, and soon there was no way of telling where sky and mountains met. There were no stars at first, yet a residue of light somehow remained, sufficient to allow them to see each other and to have more than just a memory of their immediate surroundings.

Warmth was still in the ground. Lorrimer could feel it coming into his body as he waited for Stemmle to make his move. The bandit in black had begun to snore, a low grunting sound. The other one reached into the saddlebag and pulled out the *pulque*. They heard the stopper go and dimly saw him tilt the bottle, then heard the long satisfied belching sigh.

The first of the stars pricked through. Stemmle

remained where he was, inert, apparently unconscious. The stars seemed to be switching on in groups; every few minutes Lorrimer was able to see a fraction more clearly. And the air carried a chill again, enough to make him draw into himself.

"Stemmle."

He ungummed his lips and whispered, scarcely audible, whispered and waited. The thud of his heart against the ground was louder than the word.

"Stemm . . . le."

Nothing. A fraction of the night went by. For Christ's sake. . . . Then Stemmle heaved himself into another position, coughing as he did so, disguising the fact that he nodded. Wait, wait, the nod said. His left hand was up to his face, thumb and forefinger raised. Two? Two minutes? Lorrimer's heartbeat quickened. They were in full view of the bandit on guard, only paces away, all of them tinted with the bluish light of the stars. The Springfield could be reached in four strides, Lorrimer reckoned. Already his body was flexed. Everything was beginning to bounce in and out of focus with the hammering behind his eyes. An incredible amount of time seemed to pass—seconds, lifetimes, almost unendurable. Unless Stemmle made his move in a hurry he felt the bandit would sense something.

Now, it had to be now. . . . Yet all the while a frightened part of him cowered from whatever was coming.

Stemmle took a deep breath, then started to get up. The priest's sweater was too large for him, askew on his body, like a sack. Lorrimer seemed to notice this for the first time—extraordinary what the mind selected, unreal, vivid.

Sweat came like a dam-burst through his eyebrows, blinding him. He heard Stemmle say: "I need a leak."

"Please yourself."

Lorrimer blinked furiously. Stemmle was etched against the stars, swaying slightly, a frail bent silhouette, scarcely that of someone with violence in his mind. But, even so, the bandit turned his head and brought the gun across and watched every step he took.

"That'll do."

Eighteen

Stemmle had gone about ten paces. He stood with his back toward them, and the one flaw in his pretense was that he pissed so little. He finished and turned, buttoning himself. Lorrimer didn't take his eyes off him. Right down in the roots of his mind he was mesmerized.

Stemmle shuffled a couple of yards, for all the world like someone who'd exhausted his reserves of strength.

Then he stopped and sneezed, jerking his head, hands rising to his face. Simultaneously his spectacles were dislodged and came off. He cursed feebly and dropped onto one knee, fingering the ground.

"Clumsy fool." The bandit chuckled. "Old man."

Lorrimer could see where the spectacles were, but Stemmle somehow avoided them, groping around, widening the area of search. He started to mutter, weakness and irritation compounded in the tone; but what he said was in English, meant only for Lorrimer.

"He's got . . . to come to me. . . . Got to come over." It was a sort of code. Stemmle peered about him myopically. He made weak clucking noises. "Unless he comes it's useless."

"For Christ's sake," the bandit growled, "find the things and shut up."

Stemmle didn't say anything for several seconds. He groped about, very clever about where he swept his hands, gradually turning away from the point where the spectacles had actually fallen.

"Stupid," he then said, an old distressed man, complaining to himself. "Stupid."

"You'll take all damn night," the bandit said.

"They are here . . . They must be here."

"Then find them."

The pretense went on, perhaps fifteen seconds more of it, Stemmle seemingly growing in agitation. One thing was sure; the bandit wouldn't move out of pity. But exasperation could provoke him.

"For Christ's sake," he growled again, and uncrossed his legs.

Lorrimer's scalp seemed to shrink. Stemmle had turned so that now he was standing sidelong to the bandit. The man pushed himself angrily to his feet, and in the selfsame instant Lorrimer saw Stemmle slide the knife from the bottom of his right trouser-leg; it was coolly, casually done. Actors did it like that, experts, professionals. Lorrimer stiffened, his pulse like a hammer, an awful weakness in his guts. In a moment everything was going to start happening at once.

The bandit crossed heavily to where Stemmle was, using the revolver as a pointer, the wide-brimmed hat slung like a disk behind his neck. He saw the spectacles immediately.

"There." He jabbed with the gun. "There." He kicked dirt contemptuously into Stemmle's face. *"Tonto. . . .* Another time—"

And then Stemmle made his move.

He went for the bandit from the crouch, lunging upwards. Fast though he was, the bandit saw him coming and chopped down on Stemmle's knife arm. Stemmle countered, grappling for the gun, and the bandit let out a shout.

Lorrimer was halfway to the rifle when the other bandit woke and reacted, snatching for the revolver at his waist. Lorrimer crashed into him shoulder first; a boot thudding into his face, accepting the pain, the revolver sent flying. Fear gave him strength, gave it to both of them. They rolled, grunting in the gritty dust, gouging, kicking, locked together.

With shocked awareness Lorrimer knew that Mercedes had screamed and was scrambling clear. Every instant he was expecting a shot, an end to Stemmle and then himself. He fought in dread of it, an animal in him. Once the bandit almost broke away. Lorrimer bawled at Mercedes to grab the rifle, but whether she did he couldn't tell. He heard Stemmle snarl, and then a blubbering gasp. The bandit kneed him in the groin, mad starlit eyes only inches from his own. Lorrimer gulped like someone drowning, thrashed about, no ear where his fingers clawed, pain burning like a fire.

Then his head crashed murderously against the ground. Stunned, he let go his hold, and the bandit tore free, crawling frenetically toward the revolver. Lorrimer's mind and body seemed dissociated; stupefied he watched the bandit reach the revolver and point it in his direction. In the same instant, from behind, there was a shot and the ground erupted close to the bandit's outstretched arm.

Mercedes—Lorrimer saw her on the very edge of his vision, the rifle held at her hip.

The bandit rolled and fired, rolled again and sprinted

for cover. Lorrimer gained control over himself. Life reentered his limbs. He ducked behind a chunk of rock, shouting at the girl to do the same, calling for the rifle. Sobbing for breath, he turned desperately in Stemmle's direction and was amazed to see him on his feet, he and the one called Paco.

And they were holding each other.

As he watched, he saw the bandit's embrace slacken, his knees begin to sag. The gun he carried had already fallen to the ground. Stemmle started to retreat. He put his arms around the bandit and walked slowly backwards, using him as a shield, holding him as if he loved him.

"Let him go, *curandero,*' the one in black commanded, nowhere to be seen.

"Soon."

"Now!"

Stemmle backed up a slight slope between some boulders.

"He is yours," he called abruptly; his voice was indefinably different. "All yours." Then he took his arms away and lurched from sight. The bandit's body fell with a sullen thud and a bullet screamed off the rock where Stemmle had just been.

Lorrimer snatched hold of Mercedes by the wrist and worked around to Stemmle's position, jinking in and out of cover. There was a wildness in him, and a numbness, a high-pitched singing in his ears. They went in short dashes, crouching until they got to where Stemmle was.

For the briefest of moments Lorrimer couldn't think what was different about him; then he realized that parts of him were dark and wet with blood.

They slithered among the boulders, the dead bandit hidden from them, everything suddenly hushed and eerie. In the open space where they had all been together the fallen .38 was lying in the dirt, and beyond it were the loads of money and the saddlebags containing what was left of the food and water. And beyond these again—somewhere—was the other bandit.

Stemmle breathed: "See him?"

"No."

There was more to survival than escape. They needed the contents of the saddlebags, the canteen most of all.

Lorrimer picked up a stone and tossed it high into the rocks farther up the slope, seeking to draw the bandit's fire and so locate him. But nothing happened. They waited, crouched close, nostrils flared at the smell of the blood. Separate from the abandoned items was the blanket-wrapped bundle of fuse and explosive.

"Give me the rifle," Lorrimer mouthed at Mercedes. "The rifle. . . ."

Her hands were shaking, but she'd been quick and controlled enough when it mattered. He passed the rifle on to Stemmle.

"Pump some shots into the explosive."

Stemmle hesitated. "It will blow. It will all go up."

"We'll never get back out there otherwise."

Every word was whispered. Lorrimer turned urgently to the girl and told her what to do, and when.

"Try it," he urged Stemmle. "Take a chance."

Stemmle nodded and moved from view, edging into a firing position. Lorrimer put his fingers to his ears and opened his mouth and in dumb show made Mercedes follow suit. Ten or twelve seconds elapsed before Stemmle made the first shot, hardly more, and though they were braced for it, the noise startled them.

One, two, three, four . . . the shots came on each other's heels with nothing but a whiplash crack and multi-echo to show for them. But with a fifth he must have hit a detonator. The night emptied with concussive force, scarlet on yellow. The air was sucked away and punched back at them.

"Go!" Lorrimer yelled at Mercedes.

They went together. Dust was everywhere, like a fog, and bits of debris were coming down. He stumbled into the open and sprinted for the saddlebags, a high-pitched screaming in his ears. He grabbed the saddlebags and flung them at Mercedes, then ran to the loads of money. They were too heavy to lift together and he dragged them away with him, the curdled ash-pale starlight clarifying fast, exposing him a fraction more the longer he relied on its protection.

Mercedes had retrieved the revolver. He scrambled back to the rocks which she had already reached, conscious that some of the stars had reappeared. A time would come when he remembered and relived it all, but there and then he wasn't wondering why the hell he risked himself for what was Navalosa's. And when the dead bandit's body tripped him and brought him down he went for what personally was his—reaching into the stickiness of the man's pockets to claim the dollar bills stolen from him when the odds were stacked in the bandits' favor.

"Lorrimer!"

It was the only name she knew him by. He sculled the last few yards on his elbows. Mercedes fired twice as he squirmed in beside her, both hands wrapped around the revolver, but whether she had a target or was making sure the bandit kept his head down he didn't know and didn't stop to ask.

Stemmle was nearby, reaching for the bags of gunnysacking, death smeared all over him.

"Quick . . . Quick."

The screaming still in Lorrimer's ears. He took the rifle and his share of the money load and went staggering in Stemmle's wake. To be free was incredible, like a dream, yet there was horror in it, every nerve jangling. Where they were heading didn't matter; anywhere, anywhere, to get clear—it was the same for them all.

Nobody led at first, but they kept close, and before long Lorrimer went in front. After perhaps half a mile the sense of something yapping at their heels had passed. After about three-quarters they halted and went to ground, starlight only to show them where they were, one boulder-strewn slope much the same as another.

Nothing. No one near, no one far.

Lorrimer said breathlessly: "Safe, d'you think?"

Stemmle nodded. They listened again, straining for the minutest sound.

"Anyone see him after the explosion?" He spoke in Spanish for the girl's benefit, quiet as could be. "You?"

She shook her head.

"He might have caught it. He was close enough."

"Quizá."

Stemmle said: "He's finished without water."

"So he'll hunt for us."

"Let him. He could search all night. We're safe enough." Yet they waited and listened, on and on. "Yes?"

"Bicho malo nunca muere," Mercedes said. "A vicious beast never dies."

Stemmle's response was immediate—and mistaken. "I have never killed before." He shook his hands in a strange shuddering fashion and turned to face Lorrimer. "Never," he said, back in time already, Kröhl at work on survival again, reverting to another conversation. Already. . . . And Lorrimer wasn't prepared for it, couldn't cope. It was enough to be alive. He didn't answer. Reaction was churning in his stomach and he wanted to be sick.

He stood up cautiously and stared over the broken corrugations of the mountainous wilderness they were in. Nothing. The bandit had vanished as if he had never been, only the memory of him left, the feel of the other one. An army could vanish in these hills. Ribs of strata banded a slanting outcrop and Lorrimer moved closer to it, thinking of the moon around eleven and where the shadows would fall. He was shivering a little; the air had a bite, but that wasn't the reason. The girl came and huddled beside him, no bones about it. Stemmle seemed as blind or indifferent as before, though Lorrimer wasn't so sure about this anymore: there were many Stemmles, layer upon layer, ruthless and subtle and clever and tough, all intent on one thing, capable of enormous deceptions.

Away in the night an animal howled, but their alarm was only momentary. Tides of exhaustion were overwhelming Lorrimer and the soft muscles in his thighs were quivering. Stemmle had shifted in to the overhang and was propped against the rock. The last thing Lorrimer was conscious of was Stemmle telling him again: "I'm not lying, Mister Lorrimer."

And he thought: Not now. Not that now. . . .

Time ended for him then. And it didn't begin again until the morning light spilled over the mountains and flooded the place where they were. The blood on Stemmle's clothes had dried and blackened and the awful elemental smell of it had gone as well.

Something else was different too; they weren't so in need of each other anymore. Lorrimer sensed it almost as soon as he woke and felt Stemmle's eyes on him.

Nineteen

First, though, he lived through a moment of incredulous dismay. The big tan-colored hat which belonged to the bandit Paco had been wrenched off when Stemmle discarded the body, and now Stemmle was wearing it, the shadow of the hat huge and misshapen on the ground in the sun's early level rays.

"Scare you?"

Lorrimer grunted, feeling clammy on the back of the

neck. The night's cold was in the fibers of his muscles. He moved stiffly, wincing as he did so, then drank sparingly from the canteen, rinsing the water around the way the girl had done. The revolver was beside her and the rifle was between them still; this much hadn't changed, but that was about all.

A haven of honor and excitement awaited Stemmle in Navalosa, yet his future was measured. The bandits were done with, but Riemeck remained. The thought would be aching like a cancer in him now, unceasingly. Watching him, Lorrimer considered this. Stemmle's small eyes were inflamed and beneath the leathery tan there was a constipated pallor. He looked every one of his years now, white-stubbled and shrunken, but nobody was ever what they seemed, Stemmle least of all. "I never killed before. . . ." No? The statistics could wait. But he knew how to use a knife, and the knife was still with him.

"The sooner we move, the better."

Lorrimer nodded. They ate what remained of the tortillas and saliva-ed them down. The girl ate little. She looked drained. And what she was wearing was ridiculous—blouse and skirt. Only now with morning did Lorrimer notice, free of terror, changed himself.

"Eat," he encouraged her quietly.

She shrugged.

"You will need all the strength you can find."

"I'll manage."

"Thank you for last night . . . with the rifle. You saved me then, I reckon."

Stemmle said: "That bastard in black won't ever tangle with us again." He swept a thin arm along the mountain barrier. "There's no other way he could go. Navalosa would crucify him if he came near. New ground—that's his only chance. If he's living, which I doubt."

"I hope he lives a while," the girl said. "And suffers. His kind ought to suffer."

Stemmle's gaze met Lorrimer's and jerked away. No doubt where his mind was—over the years a legion of remarks must have touched him on the raw.

They began walking, Stemmle and Lorrimer each with a halter-load of coin, Mercedes with the guns and lightened saddlebags. La Candela was an aiming point, and they made good distance at first, no furnace around them yet, no goading from behind. But Stemmle was at Lorrimer's shoulder, and soon he said a curious thing—not so much what he said as the tone he used, pique in it.

"*I* saved your life, Mister Lorrimer."

"I'm aware what you did." How freakish fate could be. "Think about it."

"What d'you want from me? . . . Thanks?"

"I want to be heard. And I want to be believed."

"I'll listen, if that's what you mean."

They were working down into the morning shadows of the canyon out of which they'd climbed yesterday stumbling and falling then, without hope then,

"I'll listen," Lorrimer repeated. "But don't forget what you asked me for when the *pistoleros* first got into the house."

"What was that?"

"My silence about your identity."

Stemmle said nothing.

"Kröhl. Lutz Kröhl, that's who you are. Within the context of that I'll listen."

Already the cord which joined the bags was cutting into the soreness of their flesh. Heavy on the leg they jarred on down, Mercedes in the rear. The sky was high-altitude blue, no clouds, a slow drift of air moving from the west.

Lorrimer said: "One more thing. Don't tell me again you never killed before."

"I didn't."

"Maybe not with a knife."

"Never."

"What was Auschwitz then? A health farm?"

"I was in an office there."

"You were responsible for the camp's administration."

"For sixteen months only."

"*Only.* In sixteen months maybe half a million—"

"I didn't kill them, Mister Lorrimer. I was not responsible for deciding whether prisoners lived or died. Or their discipline or their work programs. None of this was my responsibility."

"You were present though. Anything else is splitting hairs."

High in the wildness of Guatemala, thirty-six hours of terror behind them, and allies no longer. Lorrimer shot Stemmle an uneasy sidelong glance and thought: The bloodstains suit you.

They started to climb out of the canyon. They were sweating now, beginning to tire, pain gathering in their thighs.

"It's no good, Stemmle."

"You can't make a judgment without knowing the facts. There is more than those sixteen months to be taken into account. There is also ten years in Navalosa."

Stemmle halted. The wide-brimmed hat made him look like a different man. They all halted and took their first rest, the girl joining them. Buzzards were slow-wheeling in the sky.

"I can forget things," Stemmle said with sudden intensity. "And so can you . . . Jesus Christ, the things you must have forgotten."

"What are you trying to say?"

"Forget about me." Stemmle's look was searching. There was no sound except their voices. "Go back to where you came from and forget."

"That's not possible."

"Last night I was the only worthwhile friend you had. You owe me something."

Lorrimer nodded at Mercedes. "I owe her something too."

"The girl's neither here nor there." Stemmle used the word *muchacha* and her interest quickened; they were talking about her. "Navalosa needs me, Mister Lorrimer. Not only Navalosa. The high country, too, but Navalosa most of all. And I need Navalosa. For ten years I have been able to give something back."

"Tell Riemeck that. He's the one who's lifted the lid." Lorrimer armed a trickle of sweat from his face. "It's not just me who knows who you are."

They moved on, tension between them. Their reserves of strength were small and ebbing all the time. It would have been a mercy to themselves to ditch their dead-weight loads, but the thought was never voiced. Navalosa had beggared itself on their account and it was an obligation to return the ransom. If it was abandoned, it would remain abandoned, perhaps forever. There was no way of telling where all yesterday's stumblings and fallings had led them, or where they trod now. Sometimes La Candela was visible, sometimes not, and one barren slope or deep crevasse or boulder-strewn hillside was like another.

"I'm not what I was, Mister Lorrimer." This came from behind, as they walked. "It was thirty years ago."

"What were you?"

"Someone who went with the tide. If you didn't go with the tide in those days, you drowned."

"You more than stayed afloat. You did all right for yourself. And at the end you managed to save your own skin. You came a long way, but you survived when others didn't."

"Survival isn't a reason for living. There is something else, Mister Lorrimer. The longest journey is the journey inward."

"What am I meant to say to that?"

"Give me a chance."

They halted again, panting.

"It's not for me to give. Riemeck will have written me off. I haven't gone back to his contact so he'll assume I'm not interested. Someone else will take his story to market now. Even if I wanted to I couldn't stop him. It's a big story, Stemmle. You're merely one piece of it."

"How d'you mean?"

"Other people are mentioned." Hadn't he told him that? "Where they are, how they live."

"Who?"

"Survivors like yourself."

"I don't believe this."

"Nor did I until I checked on what was written about you."

All of Stemmle was in his eyes, everything he ever was.

"What other people?" he said again.

"Bormann . . . Mengele." Mengele would have been a colleague at Auschwitz. "Muller . . . Glucks—"

"No!"

"I was given their names."

There was silence between them. *"Qué pasa?"* the girl asked, seeming to believe their voices were raised because of her. But neither answered. Incredulity shaped every fold and line of Stemmle's face.

"Peter Riemeck would never take such an action. . . . Never."

"Who else brought me up to Navalosa?"

"It will go no further."

"That's not the feeling I came away with."

"Riemeck will change his mind." Stemmle muttered to himself in German, then glanced at Lorrimer. "He will not proceed."

Hope can be a binding, deluding thing. "You seem very sure."

"His life would be worth nothing if he did."

"His mind will be changed for him, is that it?"

"I think."

Lorrimer said: "If that's the case, there must be safety in numbers."

"Years ago, in Bolivia, someone attempted to make a move of this kind, but it never came to anything."

"No?"

"No, Mister Lorrimer."

" 'My honor is loyalty'—Riemeck's already gone back on his word."

"He'll be reminded."

"You're so sure," Lorrimer repeated. Once in the club, always in the club—was that it?

"The people you mentioned haven't survived this long merely by chance."

"How about you?"

Stemmle humped his load. "In my opinion I've only one person to worry about."

The sun lost its shape and blanched the sky. They went with blistered feet and flesh grazed raw, sweat running in an oily film. The earliest they could hope to reach the village was evening. They rested increasingly, three or four times in every hour, sometimes without shade, only Stemmle protected by the bandit's hat, the bloodshot whites of his eyes emphasized by his shadowed face.

On purpose Lorrimer yielded the lead to Stemmle; he didn't care to have him behind him now. Thirst dried their mouths and they spoke less often. But Stemmle never quite gave up, even in the furnace heat of noon.

"Forget who I was."

"Give me one good reason."

"Navalosa is the reason. There is also the fact that you owe your life to me."

"I'm not denying that."

The girl fell, not badly, but with a small cry of exhaustion. Lorrimer helped her to her feet.

Stemmle said thickly: "Forget her as well, Mister Lorrimer."

"Huh?"

"Am I blind, d'you think?"

"I don't know what you are. Two days and I'm nowhere near to finding out."

"Leave the girl alone."

"You should tell them that in Navalosa."

God knows why he said it. It was cheap and petty and stupid, and afterward he told himself he must have been weakened beyond reason even to have bothered. And he wasn't prepared for Stemmle's reaction; Stemmle was halfway to the knife before he realized what was happening. As fast as anything he ever did in his life Lorrimer dived for the rifle, reached it with the very ends of his fingers and somehow got a grip. All in the same desperate scramble of movement he managed to snatch it up and point it at Stemmle, fumbling off the safety catch.

"Drop it!"

Stemmle crouched, both hands down by his right ankle.

"Drop it, Stemmle!"

Lorrimer was on his side, arched hip and shoulder. Five thudding heartbeats passed before either he or Stemmle moved; they glared, paces apart. Then Stemmle slowly straightened. The knife dropped to the ground.

"Kick it away from you."

Stemmle obeyed and Lorrimer rose to his feet. The girl stood a little apart, her gaze darting from one to the other. This time she knew she was not mistaken, and gratification showed on her lips and in her eyes; unbelievably, with strength all but burned and starved out of her, this showed.

"Search him, Mercedes."

Lorrimer was taking no chances. He stood with the rifle leveled while the girl felt her way around Stemmle's stiffened body. Almost immediately Lorrimer wished he'd made the search himself; there was both contempt and triumph in the way she did what she'd been asked to do. And on Stemmle's emaciated face was a look of sickening accusation and despair.

"I am a prisoner then?"

Twenty

Lorrimer picked the knife out of the dust. The revolver was lying where the rifle had been, close to the saddlebags, and he picked that up as well. He hadn't answered Stemmle, and Stemmle remained where he was, still as a statue. Lorrimer didn't find it easy to look at him, at either of them.

"The day you feel pity for someone other than yourself, that'll be the day. . . ." Lay off, Sarah.

They were on a broken plateau, pumice-stone hills like a choppy sea behind them and a drop to one side down into a deep cleft. Lorrimer walked to the edge of the drop and tossed the rifle away, then the revolver, then the knife; one of them clattered and slithered for much longer than the others. Before he did all this he took the bolt out of the Springfield and emptied the live shells from the revolver and scattered them separately.

He was on his way back, still a dozen limping paces clear of the other two, when Stemmle spoke. He hadn't moved.

"I don't understand you."

Lorrimer reached the gunnysacking bags. Black specks overlaid his vision and he was light in the head, his pulse like a pile driver.

"Why?" Stemmle asked shakily.

"Maybe I'd have killed you otherwise."

The girl was staring, mystified.

" 'Maybe?' " Stemmle queried.

"It would have been you or me."

Mercedes started toward him. "Lorrimer." It sounded like a password, a sign of allegiance. But his eyes were on Stemmle.

"I came after a story," he said. "I'll settle for that. What happens to you isn't my responsibility."

"No?"

Mercedes took Lorrimer by the arm. She turned on

Stemmle. "You are not for me. Not anymore for me."

"Whose responsibility is that, Mister Lorrimer?"

"I'm not talking about her."

"She's a part of what you've done. Before you came she only dreamed. She was content with dreams. There was nothing else."

Lorrimer wasn't drawn, not again.

"And the story you write will be as effective as any bullet. It will be the end for me."

"You'll survive. You have before."

"You can die in different ways, Mister Lorrimer."

"You should know that better than most."

The girl smiled at Lorrimer, dust matting her blue-black hair. They were weak and miles from anywhere; it was a preposterous situation, and the last thing Lorrimer wanted now was to pity Stemmle again. Yet he couldn't stop himself. Just then he wasn't feeling the sun or the pains throbbing in his body and his thoughts weren't colored by the myriad slaughterhouse crimes that had turned Stemmle into a fugitive. All he was aware of in these moments was feeling sorry for him, despite every instinct warning him of the dangers.

"What is it you are after?" Stemmle moved his hands, as yellow and wasted as last year's leaves. "Justice? Is that the word you'd use?"

"I told you what I came for."

"Vengeance?"

"I told you."

"Navalosa has a right to me, Mister Lorrimer. A need and a right."

"You said that before."

Impatiently, Lorrimer separated from the girl and slung the bags of coin. He began to walk and Stemmle shouted after him, as hoarse as if a blowlamp had seared his throat.

"It's a mutual need. Have you ever heard of reparation? Lutz Kröhl is dead, Mister Lorrimer. He died a long time ago."

They didn't keep so close now; Stemmle was often trailing by all of fifty yards. The sight of La Candela led them on, but there were times when it seemed to be no nearer and other times when the heat almost water-waved it out of existence. It was two days since they'd eaten properly and they were deteriorating fast, dehydrated, the sun burning them into a state of brainlessness. It seemed to follow Lorrimer like a searchlight, shrinking his scalp over his skull, blinding him with its dazzle. There was nowhere a place to hide, no trees, no scrub ever higher than their ankles, and only Stemmle had protection under the hat of the dead bandit. He shouted intermittently from the rear, shoulders hunched, sometimes lurching off his intended course.

"I am not a *pistolero* . . . I know what I was, but I have chosen what I am."

"What are you then?"

"El curandero, el dentista, el Alemán."

The girl panted. "What is he talking about?"

Lorrimer didn't reply, so she worried him again.

"He is sick," he told her.

"I want to go with you," she said. "When you leave Navalosa I want you to take me."

"He is sick," Lorrimer repeated stubbornly, "and I'm sorry for him."

"You?"

"Yes," he said.

"Why? Why, Lorrimer?"

For a start he could have said: Because of the special torture of his loneliness, because of a decade with no one ever to acknowledge him by name, because of the insects detonating against the lamps and the rats and the silence and the thankless impassivity of those who filled his house. And because he was someone who could never be forgiven.

This most of all—never, never.

But as it was, he said none of these things, being incapable of shaping what he felt, not even sure how he had come to feel with such intensity, and certainty not trusting the experience.

"Are all journalists so cold-blooded, or are you just an insensitive exception?" All right, all right, Sarah.

He clenched his teeth and struggled on, bent over, lurching as if a deck heaved beneath him. There was a time when he would have accepted almost any responsibility without a second thought. He tried to shut his ears against Stemmle's voice but in vain. Increasingly, there was one responsibility he didn't now want to accept. Deep in the oven of his urban mind he told himself he should have retained an appetite for revenge, but this too was lacking now.

"I saved your life remember," Stemmle cried.

"And then would have murdered me."

"He's mad," Mercedes said, pleading too. "Take me with you when you go."

Oh, Christ, Lorrimer thought: whatever happened he would betray someone, something. They zigzagged up to the crest of a huge rock-strewn slope, beyond speaking, dislodged rubble skittering down. La Candela really seemed nearer at last, streaked gray and purple-green, dominating the skyline. And their shadows were starting to lengthen again, no longer printed around their feet.

Under the hat Stemmle's face had the look of a skull. There was one last share of water left, and they came together for it, lifting the canteen to their swollen lips, eyes leaden, trembling as if in the grip of fever. An enormous effort was required for Lorrimer to get moving again, and he had to bully the others, dredging the remnants of will and strength.

"Four or five hours. . . . Come on, come on. Nobody's going to do it for you."

His tongue couldn't shape the words properly; without

water the second bandit must surely have died. They
abandoned the empty canteen but not the loads, never
those. Sometimes they straggled so much they were almost in danger of losing contact, but fear of separation
always brought them back to one another. To be alone
would be terrible. They went perhaps for another hour,
deep in the stupor of their desperations. And still, from
time to time, Stemmle argued his cause, wanting the
mercy Kröhl had denied others.

"What are you going to do, Mister Lorrimer?"

"I don't know."

"Forget about me?"

"I don't know."

"Between Macinta and the mountains there is no other
dentist, no other *curandero.*"

"Shut up."

"Only me."

"Tell Riemeck. Sing your song to him."

"There are unborn children who will live because of
me. And women and men who—"

"Never a thought for yourself—of course, of course."

"Listen, Mister Lorrimer—"

"Shut up!"

Croaked back and forth at each other. And somewhere
in a burning recess of his brain Lorrimer was clinging to
the need to pity him.

"You and me, Lorrimer," the girl said. "He is old.
Finished."

The sun eased down a little more and a flock of small clouds gathered in the west to await it. The slow drift of air from behind their backs had long since ceased; now everything was still, not even quivering in the heat anymore. La Candela was imperceptibly nearer, but Navalosa remained invisible and the volcano was the only recognizable landmark. As far as Lorrimer was concerned everything was beginning to haze over. This was the world, the real world, and they were in it, but he was rapidly losing any sense of time and distance.

For a while they went where a defile took them, dwarfed by the depth of its walls, shadowed at last but with the heat trapped in there with them. Later they climbed a hogback and later still there was an area where the ground was cratered and the surface crunched like clinker under their weight.

No trail anywhere, no sign of anyone ever having come this way before. Yet Navalosa couldn't be so very far. Sundown ought to see them there—surely? Surely?

Cactus sprouted from a rock fissure and the girl broke some of it off. They mashed it under their heels and all three chewed the sour white pulp for its moisture, chewed and spat out the pith and went lurching on. They were going to survive; they were surer now. The light was still strong, but at last there was coolness like silk on their skins and, miraculously, they were finding a little more of themselves still left to give.

For the moment La Candela had disappeared. Ahead

of them was a saw-edged ridge with stumpy pillars of rock exposed on its flank. Beneath its surface of dust the ground was iron-hard and treacherous, slippery juts of crag making a foothold difficult. Time and again one or the other of them went down, Mercedes near to weeping, her eyes sunken, hands and knees torn. Twice on the climb to the ridge they were forced to rest, staring like strangers at one another, gasping like swimmers come up late for air.

"The girl's no use to you, Mister Lorrimer."

Cut it out.

"She is like a child. All she has known is the high country."

Lorrimer looked away. There were so many Stemmles, past and present; he couldn't decide where pity began and abhorrence ended. The man was a chameleon, but if there was a flaw in the intricacies of his makeup it was the latter-day innocence. If anything was genuine it was this. "She dishonors him, *señor*"—he remembered the words of the priest's housekeeper—"it is common knowledge."

Lorrimer was almost beyond the reach of emotion, but a blurred sensation of guilt touched him. Already it seemed an impossible time ago since he first came to Navalosa. What kind of hungry person was he then? Somewhere in the scrambled labyrinth of his exhaustion Sarah was waiting in the wings, ready to remind him, and he shook his head. God, how he wished he was a simple man.

Clumsily he found himself helping Mercedes to her feet. Stemmle watched them with a haunted bloodshot stare, then grunted and pushed himself up, teeth bared as he lifted the heavy gunnysacking bags.

What happened after that began before Lorrimer was really aware of it. First, Stemmle did a little stumbling dance, the kind he'd done feebly a dozen times before. A split second later he clutched with both hands to his chest like a fullback taking a high ball. In the selfsame instant it seemed to Lorrimer that he went absolutely rigid and began to sink at the knees. And the blood had spurted between his clenched fingers before Lorrimer heard the crisp bark of the shot, spun around and flattened.

Twenty-one

The sound frayed into the distances and nothing bounced it back. Lorrimer was down now, the girl too, spread-eagled, down as soon as Stemmle fell. All he could immediately think of was the bandit, the one in black, presumed dead; and the fact that he'd tossed their guns away.

"Stemmle?"

Nothing.

"Stemmle?"

Up the slope among the weathered stumps of rock someone was waving, and he wasn't alone; Lorrimer saw others—three, four, breaking cover. They wore a sort of uniform and carried rifles.

"Militia," the girl said tersely.

Lorrimer hesitated, then rolled to where Stemmle had jack-knifed over. He wasn't alive anymore. His own bright blood spread glistening among the blackened traces of the last of those he had killed, and already his gray-stubbled face bore some of the ageless calm of the dead.

Lorrimer's impressions were ultravivid and compressed, as if time had somehow turned back on itself.

On a reflex he called: "He's dead, Mercedes." What he expected from her he didn't know, but afterward all he could remember was the intensity of her return glance, whole worlds in its depths beyond his comprehension. In one and the same moment he heard someone running. Looking up, he saw the first of the militiamen closing on them fast, leather bandoliers flapping, rifle brandished excitedly on a bent right arm.

"We got him, *señor*. We got him—yes?"

The militiaman crunched to a halt, dust swirling, and straddled Stemmle's body, then turned it onto its back with his boot.

"*Ayeeee.*" He stared for a few seconds, savoring his triumph. Then he said: "So . . . so." He wore a corporal's stripes, this one. Five companions were thudding down to join him, small dark-skinned men like himself, their gray-green uniforms sweat-stained and ill-fitting. Panting, the corporal said to Lorrimer: "What became of the other *pistolero?*"

Lorrimer heard himself answer: "One was killed." He was feeling nothing about Stemmle, nothing either way—just startled; there had been no warning.

"Ah," the corporal said. Then he frowned. "We were told there were three of you."

"So there were."

"Where is the second man, *señor?*"

"This is the second man." Lorrimer jerked his head like a boxer, nodding at Stemmle. "You just shot him."

It was strange to feel nothing, to realize why Stemmle was suddenly dead and not even to be angered by the stupidity of it.

"But this is a *pistolero, señor*. We were told—"

"You're wrong. He had the misfortune to be wearing the *pistolero*'s hat."

"Who is he then?" The corporal faltered.

"*El curandero,*" Lorrimer said. "*El dentista. . . . El Alemán.*"

"No!"

The militiamen gazed at Stemmle's peaceful abandon with bewildered disbelief. Then the corporal said in a distressed tone: "Oh, Jesus Christ . . . oh, Mother of God, what has happened?" He wheeled on Lorrimer, stumbling into a litany of explanations. "We are from Macinta, *señor*. All we were given was a rough description.

The priest in Navalosa told us of one dressed in black, all in black, and another with a big hat like a cattleman's—"

"Wounded in the shoulder and bandaged?"

"Yes, *señor.*"

"Was *he* wounded?" No anger even then—everything had been too sudden.

"No, *señor.* But at seventy meters the hat seemed enough. With *pistoleros, señor,* you don't take chances. He made a good target from the rocks. . . . Oh, Jesus Christ," the corporal said again, all nerves and dismay, "we should have waited until you were closer. But he was irresistible as he got to his feet, and what I feared—"

"Keep it for the priest."

"But, *señor*—"

"Keep it for the priest."

Lorrimer turned sharply away, more shocked than he knew. Somewhere in the tatters of his mind he was aware that a freak of chance had finally seen justice done and that his conscience was all at once off the hook. He looked down at what had taken thirty years to bring about and existed through a momentary hysteria, possessed at many levels.

"Bring the horses," the corporal ordered.

It was still beyond Lorrimer what the girl was thinking. Tears would have been false and despicable, but there was a part of him which expected something; Stemmle for her was no one but Stemmle, old and inadequate, over the hill. Even that was worthy of something.

Wearily he asked the corporal, "How long to Nava-losa?"

"No more than ten kilometers."

"You didn't search far."

"Where horses could go, *señor,* we have been. For twenty-four hours we have covered what ground we could. We were on our way back when we saw you and your friend."

"He was not my friend. He helped to save my life, but he was not my friend."

Lorrimer checked himself, in danger of protesting too much, aware of that danger. Mercedes went to Stemmle's side and pulled away the bags of coin. For a moment she paused to look at him, absolutely impassive, and again Lorrimer wondered what was behind the mask. Then he saw the horses being led down from the stumpy rock pillars higher up, six of them, hardly bigger than ponies. They were tired and skinny, in need of water, their coats matted.

"*Señor,*" the corporal complained, thinking ahead, "if only someone from Navalosa had come with us."

"Why go on?" Lorrimer snapped. "He's dead, isn't he? You made a mistake and he's dead. That's all there is to it."

The rim of the sun had touched the peaks, and the light was beginning to thicken. The militiamen laid Stemmle across one of the horses and tied him so that his body wouldn't slide; they did it expertly enough to suggest they'd handled corpses before. With him they secured the loads of ransom money. A second horse was made available for Lorrimer and Mercedes, and the displaced militiamen also rode tandem.

"Make sure to take the *pistolero*'s hat," the corporal commanded. "They must be shown in Navalosa how easy it was to be mistaken."

The horses moved at a walk, picking their way in atrocious conditions. Behind them the purple mountains were tipped with flame. Stemmle was at the rear, towed by a militiaman on a leading rein. For a longish while in the shrinking light no word passed between anybody. The girl's hands were on Lorrimer's hips, no pressure, just for balance, and they rode in silence like the rest. Fear wasn't waiting to spring at him anymore. Relief had long since come and gone and left him limp, yet while fear existed his thoughts were in a straitjacket. Now his feelings were all confused and he was too depleted in strength and spirit to believe he could cope.

One thing he already knew, however. Navalosa was the loser. "Lutz Kröhl is dead, Mister Lorrimer"—good riddance. But Stemmle was dead as well now and it seemed a waste, a Pyrrhic victory. "He's mad," Mercedes had said. So he was once, thirty years ago, worse than mad. Yet nothing could compensate for a million victims. Death itself was easy, too easy, a release, whereas life at the level Navalosa offered was anything but that. And

Navalosa needed him. The living had had a claim on him, too.

It was no use calling the corporal a fool. And anyway, what right had he to blame anyone? Hadn't he come up from Macinta himself with Stemmle's end in mind?

They traveled in the evening's cool along the spine of a ridge, eyes adjusting as the last of the day curdled into darkness. There was just the sound of the horses walking and the creak of leather.

The girl said: "When will you go, Lorrimer?"

His mind hadn't begun to bother itself with questions like that.

"Tomorrow?"

"Probably."

The world was in her heart already and he'd helped to put it there. Dishonor was not a word he cared for, yet this was the punishment she had inflicted on Stemmle—not just that one fierce time when Lorrimer had used her like a whore, but whenever it suited her. And if Stemmle had lived she wouldn't have changed her ways. There would have been no joy for him if he'd been spared, no solace, no dignity. "Dentist's woman. . . ." Just work to do, day in, day out, and loneliness, and all the horrors from half a lifetime away that could never be obliterated.

Death was an escape. And a waste. Anyone could die.

"Where will you go?"

"Guatemala City to begin with."

He wasn't really listening, even to what he himself said.

Macinta, San Camilo, Guatemala City. Then Mexico City. Then home. . . . Incredibly, England was just across the sky.

They still had with them in the cloth saddlebags the bottle of tequila. Lorrimer drank from it and the girl took a little herself, swigging from the bottle as they rode. Ahead, the lead horse whinnied, a shrill shivering sound, yet it hardly brushed Lorrimer's memory; his brain seemed filled with gray mud. It was quite dark, though already the star scatter was beginning to show and the huge mass of La Candela loomed against it. At one point the corporal pulled out of the line and waited until he could ride alongside Lorrimer and Mercedes. He questioned them about the bandits: the one who was killed— and how, and by whom—and the one who got away.

"You had all the luck, *señor*. You and the *señorita*. Only your friend was unlucky."

Lorrimer let it pass.

"It was stupid of him to wear the hat," the corporal said, some of his poise recovered, extracting himself from the center of blame. "Ridiculous and stupid. I am sorry to say such a thing, but it is true. It is almost as if he were inviting something to happen."

"That's nonsense," Lorrimer replied, and he knew he spoke the truth. "The *curandero* wanted more than anything to live."

It was all of an hour after sundown before they saw the

glimmer of Navalosa, a yellow smudge on the early silver of the night.

"Take me with you when you go," the girl said over Lorrimer's hunched back, rocking to the same aching rhythms.

"You would hate me."

"Please."

"Within a month you would hate me."

"Never."

He didn't care for what he had begun to feel about himself. He was sodden through with exhaustion, but his defenses were down and he reckoned he didn't much like what he was—and had never really been what he liked. How about that, Sarah? How about that then? . . . He was a long way from understanding, a long way from anything crystal clear. What had happened had happened, and a little more must happen yet, but a lesson was never too late for the learning. Mercy was what the world needed most.

They came in file over the crest which rimmed Navalosa around and entered the cultivated area which sustained it. All the time the lights of the place were separating, taking on individual identities, and soon they were back again in the narrow ways between adobe walls and thatch and rusted tin roofs. The ancient smells were waiting for them, the sounds of habitation. The corporal rode at the head of the file, and for two or three turns there was no one but themselves in the tight maze leading to the *plaza*.

Then a boy stood staring, wheeled and scampered ahead. Then amazed voices started to reach them out of doorways, windows, alleys.

"They are back! Look, look—they have come back!"

The quick-thrown echoes of the clatter of the horses were joined by a rising murmur. All eyes were on Stemmle and his rag-doll homecoming.

"The *curandero* is dead!"

Now there were people running, pushing, emerging from the *cantina,* God knows where. And the murmuring grew into a babble, a crescendo of shock and dismay, spreading into the *plaza* before the corporal brought the column of horses out in front of the church.

"They are back among us, and the *curandero* is dead!"

Twenty-two

The priest came bursting out of the church, the doors still yawning slowly inwards as his eagerness brought him to the top of the steps. "The *curandero* is dead"—he couldn't have heard properly. But now he saw for himself, and it stopped him between strides. His arms were outstretched and they remained so, dismay shrinking the exuberance of the gesture as his eyes locked on Stemmle's roped body.

"Corporal?" he faltered.

"It is true, *padre.*"

The cry was going out of the *plaza,* spreading into the alleys beyond the granary, and the priest listened to the voices, motionless for seconds on end.

"God in heaven."

He blessed himself, an appalled gesture, then started down.

"The *curandero* made the mistake of wearing the hat of one of the men you described." The corporal slid off his horse. "This is the worst day of my life, *padre.* The *pistoleros* did not kill him. We had that misfortune, but in fairness it must be stated that the *curandero* was partly responsible."

The priest paid no attention. He had gone to where two of the militiamen were finishing taking the ropes off Stemmle and he helped them lift the body away from the horse. A couple of dozen people were pressing around, and the horses steamed in the night air, nostrils flaring at the nearness of water, restless.

"Where, *padre?*" the militiamen asked him.

"Take him into the church."

"We have the money, *padre,*" the corporal said, anxious to earn a merit mark. "Every coin is returned intact."

The priest seemed deaf to that as well. The militiamen had reached the top of the steps when he suddenly changed his mind. He checked them, agitated and impulsive.

"Lay him there. . . . There, yes."

Moments later he had vanished into the church and the

bell started to clang. Lorrimer and the girl dismounted. They were back where all the terror had been and all the sacrifices had been made, and now the people were crowding into the *plaza* as before. The two militiamen placed Stemmle awkwardly in front of the star-green doors, then stood aside. Others led the horses to the fountain and let them drink.

Presently the bell came to rest in its mounting and the jarring urgency of its summons died on the ears. The priest emerged into the open again and looked down at Stemmle's neatly placed body. He shook his head. People were crowding the *plaza* now, flocking in, squeezing up to the wide flight of steps.

"Friends," the priest began, hands held high. "Friends of the *curandero*. . . ."

The rustle of voices died sharply. Only the horses slobbered on, noisy in their relief.

"You will know the worst," the priest was shouting. "The militia have brought him back to us, but not alive."

The corporal offered another sop. Loudly he said: "The *pistoleros* paid for what they did to you here."

"What use is death to anyone?" A priest lived closer to death than most: the rebuke was sharp. "And the death of this man is a tragedy. . . . Tell them, corporal, how he came to be killed."

He hadn't missed much, after all. The corporal hesitated.

The priest went on: "How and where and when do not really matter; explanations cannot restore him to us.

What is done is done. But we are entitled to the truth."

Reluctantly the corporal mounted the steps. He faced the crowd and cleared his throat and limped into an explanation of what had happened, lifting the bandit's hat for all to see. A murmuring rose up, many voices together, some louder and more critical than others. The corporal coped as best he could, but he was not a man of words and the priest soon intervened.

"Do not add anger to your grief. That would be wrong and unjust."

He paused. He seemed very moved, looking like a scarecrow in his *peón's* clothes.

"The world will always have its *pistoleros,* but Navalosa will never again have a *curandero* like this one. Pray for him with me."

He began a prayer and everybody joined in, a ragged chorus that filled the *plaza.* When the prayer was over he prayed alone and aloud in another tongue.

Then he called out: "Later he will go into the church, and tomorrow we will do for him what must be done. But now, if you wish it, you can offer him respect. Now while sorrow is freshly in your hearts."

A line began to form, guided by the militiamen. Nobody held back. People started to file by, men and women of every age, mounting the steps diagonally and going past Stemmle wth a nod or a sort of curtsey or just a long parting stare.

Lorrimer didn't follow them; he knew how Stemmle looked. Good-bye, Stemmle, good-bye, Kröhl. . . . You escaped everyone in the end—those who wanted you and those who needed you and those who were ready to discard you. But life was the kind of vengeance you most deserved. Here, the way it was, the way it would have continued.

Chance should have spared you for that. I think I would have done.

He turned in the starlight and left the physical pressures and hushed whisperings of the crowd. Latecomers plucked at him—"What happened, *señor?* Is it true the *curandero* was killed by mistake?" He got away from them. "Ask the corporal," he answered. "Ask the priest." All he could think of was sleep. He started across the *plaza,* and the girl must have seen him. By the granary she had caught him up.

"Where are you going?"

"The priest's house."

A child was gazing at him out of a woman's eyes. "Even if he had lived, I would not be with him now."

"Look," Lorrimer began, fatigue ingrained in every cranny of mind and body. "Leave it, can't you, Mercedes?"

"You wanted me once."

"That was when—"

"As long as he lived you wanted me."

He frowned. She gestured toward the faraway mountains.

"Out there. Until the last you and he were at each other."

He took a few paces and she followed.

"You were rowing about me."

"Not entirely."

"In the house, too—at the beginning."

"No."

"Of course it was me. Who else? At the beginning you were strangers."

He shrugged. Her eyes were velvet black in the starry darkness. "I forget," he said. "I can't remember."

They were out of the *plaza* now. Some villagers hurried by, but Lorrimer and the girl might not have been there. Nobody mattered except Stemmle.

She said: "Have you forgotten how it was when we were going for the guns?"

"No. And I won't."

"I was useful to you then. Does that deserve good-bye?"

"There always has to be a good-bye. Better here than somewhere you don't know." Bastard, he thought. He touched her, his reserves all but gone, emotionally barren. "The world isn't the place you think it is. Nothing like it, nowhere near."

"You said I would hate you in a month."

"Very likely."

"You were wrong. I hate you now."

He nodded. He could believe it.

"Better to hate me here," he told her, "than to find it out when you're somewhere you don't belong."

She limped away from him, bitterness and resignation dulled by exhaustion. Yesterday was dead and gone and tomorrow was out of sight, yet here and now had ceased to matter. It was a bad way for anything to end. Lorrimer watched her going away, numb right through, then turned and made the remembered zigzag to the house of the priest. No one came to answer when he thumped on the door, so after a while he discovered a way around to the back and finally got in through a window.

The hard bed in the cell-like room he thought of as his own was the softest thing he had ever experienced. And he was asleep before he'd even kicked off what was left of his shoes.

Morning stabbed bright on his eyes and eventually woke him. There wasn't a part of him that didn't burn with aching. Stiffly he pushed onto his elbows and surveyed himself—the torn clothes, the broken nails, the bruised and blistered skin. He fingered the soreness of his face beneath its thickened stubble and remembered everything he'd endured since he'd last lain on this bed— and knew with certainty that, even if he wanted to, he was never going to forget. "The longest journey is the journey inward"—least of all that.

Monday? Was it Monday now?

He went out to the pit, then washed himself, then came back in and took a change of clothes from his grip. Their freshness was like balm on his body. The bat-faced woman in the house had heard him moving about, and when he came into the main room there was coffee waiting for him, with beans and tortillas. After today, he promised himself, he would never eat tortillas again; but he was ravenous now and ate everything she put before him.

"Good, *señor?*"

"*Gracias.*"

She watched him discreetly from a corner of the shabby room in which he had first heard Stemmle mentioned after reaching Navalosa—a good man, a fine man, with respect for those who suffer. . . . How long ago it seemed, yet how lasting the sense of irony; that, too, would never leave him. *Stemmle? Stemmle?* He could recall his incredulity even now.

"He was a legend in these parts," the woman said, stepping forward to fill Lorrimer's cup. "God must have been looking the other way."

"He often does." He knew of a million times, Kröhl times.

"For what reason, *señor?*"

"The priest must tell you what the answer is."

"Often," she said between her greasy black plaits, "there are more questions than answers."

Always, he thought, but left it unsaid; he had done enough damage here.

He finished eating and returned to his room to pack his grip. The radio was putting out a newscast, and he straightened up at the mention of Navalosa. ". . . Early last night a patrol of mounted militia based at Macinta returned to Navalosa with the body of one of three hostages taken at gunpoint from the village by bandits. The dead man was a Guatemalan citizen by the name of Karl Stemmle, aged about sixty, who for ten years or more had worked in Navalosa as a dentist and medical practitioner. Details are still lacking, but it is understood that the other two hostages are safe. . . ."

Someone must have hurried down to Macinta during the night. The world was suddenly small again, eavesdropping on everywhere else. Lorrimer wondered for a moment whether Riemeck would have heard the story yet and what he would do when he did; he'd lost his prize sample. "The accuracy of what I have in my possession will whet your appetite for more." That go-between of his with the uneasy eyes and frayed pink cuffs would need a new exhibit now.

"Are you leaving us, *señor?*"

He hadn't heard the priest come in. "That's right." He nodded.

"But you should rest. After what you have been through—"

"I'll manage."

"When will you go?"

"Almost immediately." Lorrimer flicked a rueful smile. "I didn't expect to stay as long as I have."

The priest made a fluttering gesture of apology. "Last night, *señor,* when you returned, I was so distressed that I did not manage even a word with you to say how relieved and grateful I was that you had come to no harm."

"Thank you, but it was the last thing I expected."

"To have lost the *curandero* is like an amputation, *señor.*

He has gone, but we still feel the pain. All of us." He clucked his tongue in misery. There was a swelling on the side of his neck where the bandit had struck him with the pistol-butt. "And what a way for it to have happened, when he—and you—had survived so much."

"And the girl."

"The three of you."

Reminded, Lorrimer fumbled in his pocket for the Mexican dollars the bandit Paco had stolen from him. The corners were brown with blood. He kept half for himself; the other half he handed to the priest.

"Would you see that she gets these?"

"Of course."

"She asked to come with me. Frankly, it's not a responsibility I want to accept."

With difficulty he matched the priest's gaze; it was very steady, very shrewd. "You are more honest than some, *señor.*"

"Late in the day."

"You should dislike yourself a little, all the same."

"I do," Lorrimer said. "At the very least I do that."

How Sarah would have laughed. He picked up the grip, remembered the camera. The priest said he would accompany him as far as the *plaza*, and they went together into the brilliance of midmorning, dogs sniffing the gutters, a few people on the move.

"When do you bury Stemmle?"

"This evening. . . . He was not one of mine, *señor,* if you

244

follow me, but this is where he belonged. And I had his permission."

"He spoke about it?"

"Once upon a time. Only saints are supposed to be indifferent to their personal futures."

With what he thought was cunning, Lorrimer said, "Wasn't he one of those?"

And the priest answered carefully, "I always thought of the *curandero* as a man who was molded by a sense of guilt."

Twenty-three

Lorrimer slowed, startled. "What do you mean?" He could hear himself. "Guilt? Guilt about what?"

"I couldn't say."

"Then how—?"

"He was not an easy person to know, *señor*. In many respects he remained a stranger. But nobody comes to a place like Navalosa without a reason. For instance, you told us you were here because of La Candela. Very well, I accept that. And not so long ago there was a man here who said he was a prospector. I accept that, too—why not? But the *curandero* never gave a reason, not once in all the years."

"Didn't you ask him for one?"

"No."

"Why not?"

"Partly because when I came myself he was already established. And partly because I was always afraid of what his reply would be." They were entering the *plaza,* turning where the bandits had led them. "He had reached a stage of permanency, *señor.* And we needed him. Self-interest makes cowards of us all. He might have left us, you see, if I had probed too much."

"What d'you suppose he had turned his back on?"

"It could have been anything."

"You sound as if you've no doubt at all."

"One puts two and two together. What does a man run away from? You could make a hundred guesses and still be wrong." The priest narrowed his eyes. "The sins of omission are also ones we live to regret, and I see now I should have spoken to him. We have lost him anyway, and he might—who knows?—have welcomed the chance of talking. . . . But I tell you, *señor.* The past is the sun gone down. Today is what we have to live with—and guard against."

They halted in front of the church, where fear had hollowed everyone out and made them search into themselves. Women were burning incense on the steps now, and off to one side men had set up a table and were sorting out the bags of money. There was no trading under the covered sidewalks.

"God go with you," the priest said, offering his hand. "Where will you be tonight?"

"San Camilo."

"And tomorrow night?"

"Mexico City."

Envy was resurrected in the priest's sad eyes and was disciplined away. "Think of us sometimes in Navalosa. All of us. And of your burned-out volcano." The handshake was firm. "Good-bye now."

So Lorrimer started down, and almost at once he knew he was a fool not to have rested more. As he passed through the alleys that took him out of Navalosa there were those who greeted him with grave little nods and gestures, but he wasn't Stemmle and it was Stemmle they had wanted to buy back.

He soon left the fringes of the village behind and followed the paths among the untidy patterns of crops and stunted pines. On the brink of the ridge that would hide Navalosa from him forever he took a last return look; the village seemed even smaller than the first time it had showed itself, but on the map of his mind's eye it was already indelibly positioned.

The militia patrol had ridden down before him; there were fresh droppings on the way, and he kicked himself for not having thought of fixing a ride. It surprised him how weak he was, how quick to tire. Every few hundred yards he had to shift the grip from one hand to the other, and every quarter mile or so it was necessary to rest. But there was no climbing, thank God, nothing worse than the heat and the jarring and how long it took. The rutted track was his and his alone all the way to Macinta, and once in a while an empty stream-bed or a narrow defile or a vast ash-gray vista prodded his memory, but for the most part he wasn't much aware of his surroundings.

He reached Macinta around one o'clock. The place was sunk in lethargy and the bus to San Camilo didn't leave until four. It was already there, frying in the sun at the spot where it had put him down the other day, but four in the afternoon was the time of departure. . . . *Sí, señor.* Lorrimer found somewhere to slake his thirst, then went back to the oven of the bus, picked a slatted seat within the wheelbase and promptly fell asleep. The hubbub of departure roused him. He stirred and vaguely looked around, paid his fare, gazed at the leathery faces of the few who came to travel with him, then slept again, undisturbed by a bone-shaking vibration and the constant crashing of gears.

When he next awoke, they were almost into San Camilo. For the second time in his life he entered the town toward dusk and found himself in the square close to the remembered ceiba tree and the stalls where he'd bought the pods of chili and naïvely thought he might fool a man who had fooled the world.

"*Señor*," the driver asked as Lorrimer dismounted,

"weren't you in Navalosa when the *pistoleros* took it over?"

"I was, yes."

"The militia are back in Macinta and are saying nothing. But there have been reports on the radio." He wasn't the same driver as before. "I guessed it was you, *señor.* . . . Were you present when the *curandero* was killed?"

"I'd rather not talk about it."

Stemmle's legend would stretch at least this far; death had made more than just the high country all his own.

"Sorry," Lorrimer said curtly, moving. "The militia know what happened up there better than anyone."

He crossed to the *pension* and slapped the brass bell on the counter in the lobby where an image of the Virgin was nailed to the wall. The same half-breed woman appeared and gazed stolidly at him as if she'd never seen him in her life. "A room? There is a room, of course. . . ." Only on the stairs did she admit to his having been there before. "Did you find your way to Macinta, *señor?*"

He took it as a sign that he was beginning to escape. Later he went in search of food and a shave and a new pair of shoes. The sky was dark now, mosquitoes about, yellow lights in the market, garbage and jetsam on the broken sidewalks, the air spiced with the scent of herbs. He ate where he'd eaten the other time, then he bought some shoes and found a barber; the shoes weren't much, but good enough. He was restless yet still weary, too much cramming his mind, wanting to be gone from here, farther on his way, yet somehow unprepared for the future and its freedom.

In the night he dreamed of Stemmle and existed with Mercedes and relived the nightmare in the *plaza* when the explosive hung between them from the fuse across their throats. He woke with a strangled shout, sweating from the feel and smell of it, terror as real and close as the shadows on the bare wall beside his bed. He lay for a very long time before he was calm enough to sleep again, and even when all sense of menace had finally gone out of him memories of himself remained.

In the morning a second bus took him to Guatemala City—all chrome and glass, this one, smooth and soft-cushioned on the twisting highway. Everything was different here; water flowed on the riverbeds and the land was green, intensively worked. Navalosa receded mile by mile, but it did not diminish; in one sense, Lorrimer already knew, there could never be an escape. They cruised, with music playing to make the journey more agreeable for the tourists traveling down from north of the border. Other volcanoes showed themselves, other mountains, other towns, but there was only one place in his mind's eye. Three hours after leaving San Camilo they reached the capital, and an hour and forty minutes after arriving at the airport Lorrimer was boarding a flight to Mexico City.

He dozed a little then, on and off. Somewhere over Mexico he bought cigarettes from a blond stewardess with painted eyes.

"What have you done to your hands?"

He looked at the grazes as if for the first time.

"Did you have a fall or something?"

"Both," he said.

They were down on time with a thud of wheels and the reverse-thrust's roar. Customs wasn't interested in Lorrimer's grip. He took a taxi to the Alameda Hotel and was lucky enough to be offered a cancellation.

"For how many nights, *señor?*"

"One," he said.

Eight days ago he'd been on the point of flying home and now—tomorrow—he would go. "Mister Lorrimer? Mister Anthony Lorrimer?" Just here the man had touched him on the sleeve. He was the very last person Lorrimer wanted or expected to see again, but he bought a paper on his way up to his room and the man's photograph leaped at him off the folded page like something meant for him and him alone.

MYSTERY KILLING

Lorrimer froze, stock-still.

Rafael Gomez, found murdered today in his apartment on the Calle de San Vicente. Police estimate he had been dead for at least two days. The dead man, who was strangled, had put up a violent resistance before being overcome and his apartment ransacked. From information in police possession it is believed the deceased was an insurance agent with international connections. Inquiries are proceeding.

The narrow face looking out at Lorrimer was as furtive-eyed as when they'd first met in the Café Monterrey. Flat ears, lipline mustache, brackets hooked deep around the mouth. Yet a doubt remained, no more than a trace, but enough to send Lorrimer to the telephone. He had memorized the number he was to have called and he rang it at once, not from his room but from a booth in the foyer, wits about him for a change.

"Yes?"

He remembered the voice as he remembered the face, and this wasn't it.

"Who's that speaking?" he asked.

"Police."

He hung up and took the elevator back to his floor. The paper was where he'd hurriedly tossed it down, and once more he studied the coarse-screen picture, read the caption through like lightning.

"My honor is loyalty"—Stemmle was right, after all. Once in the club, always in the club. "Riemeck will be reminded, Mister Lorrimer. The people you have mentioned haven't survived this long merely by chance. . . . And as for myself, in my opinion I have only you to worry about."

Gomez and Riemeck were one and the same; from the first the thought had been there.

Lorrimer went to the window and stared out. He was weary of death and all the ways there were of dying, in the body and in the mind and in the heart, too close to every part of it. But emotion was trembling in him, waiting its chance to be uncaged. There was a story to be written and his debt to Stemmle no longer got in the way. For the present, though, it could wait; a day or two more it could wait. All that really mattered was going back to where he belonged, and a sense of homesickness was as good as anything to get him started.

"Cold fish," Sarah used to say. "You're empty."

No, he thought, and smiled a little. Not anymore. Never again.